SETH PARKER'S HYMNAL

Compiled by

Phillips H. Lord

as

SETH PARKER

Price $1.00

Fourth Edition

CARL FISCHER Inc. COOPER SQUARE NEW YORK

Made in U. S. A.

Dedicated to

Everybody—Everywhere

I wish to thank the Rodeheaver Publishing Company for its permission to use the copyright material which is found in this book

SETH PARKER

SETH PARKER

JONESPORT
MAINE

4 W. 40th STREET
NEW YORK

1532326

Dear Folks:

I've had a real good time getting these old hymns together and I hope you enjoy singing them as much as we do.

You'll find in the book here most of the old tunes, but of course there'll be a couple now and then that you'll think ought to be in, but aren't. Now if I was suggesting I'd say to kick just about enough to get a dollar's worth of enjoyment out of it, but not so much so you won't enjoy the other tunes that you do find. Some folks try to get a twenty-dollar kicking license out of just one dollar, but of course that isn't in proportion.

One thing about singing these old tunes is they make everybody feel as if they were neighbors. A neighbor is a man, you know, who tries to make living a mite more fun for everybody and when a man gets feeling this way he's pretty sure to catch religion. One thing to remember, though, is that if you're a neighbor it doesn't make much difference what color the church is painted that the other neighbor goes to. If he's a good neighbor you can feel sure he's got a pretty good religion, too. The proof of the tree is the taste of the apples.

Most cordial,

Seth Parker

Phillips Haynes Lord the Creator of Seth Parker

PHILLIPS HAYNES LORD is the son of Dr. Albert J. Lord, minister of the First Congregational Church of Meriden, Connecticut. He was born in Hartford, Vermont, July 13, 1902, but within a year the family had moved to Meriden.

As a boy Mr. Lord spent his summers in Ellsworth, Maine, and the greater part of this time was given to riding throughout the countryside with his grandfather, Hosia B. Phillips, who was one of the old school of New England gentlemen. As they rode together in the old buggy, his grandfather told him of folks he had known and it was Mr. Lord's privilege to meet many of these characters who lived miles off the beaten track. It was on these rides that he came to know and understand the men of the soil to such an extent that he has been able to interpret their philosophy of life with an accuracy which no other writer has yet done.

In 1925 Mr. Lord graduated from Bowdoin College at Brunswick, Maine. He was unusually quick in his studies, but did not lead his class because his interests were many and diversified. He was athletic, full of mischief, loved to do business on the side, and in other words, was just a plain full-blooded American young man. In talking with a classmate we find that his outstanding characteristics at this time were one hundred percent fight and determination to win whatever he went into, and an unlimited amount of vitality.

Although Mr. Lord was not a scholar by nature, he was appointed principal of the Plainville High School in Plainville, Connecticut, four days after graduation. He was then only twenty-two years old, but he had heard of the opportunity and went after it with the same enthusiasm and disregard for obstacles which had marked his college career. Perhaps his determination was whetted by the fact that his girlhood sweetheart, Sophia Mecorney, was teaching in the grammar school of the same town, but the fact remains he was appointed to the position, married Miss Mecorney two weeks later, and in the fall both Mr. and Mrs. Lord started instructing at the high school.

Of how Mr. Lord came to New York two years later, not knowing a soul in the city, and of his fight to break into writing, you have probably read, but the part we are most interested in is how Seth Parker finally was born.

One evening Mr. Lord happened to hear a radio program with a country setting and immediately realized it was not genuine. Sitting down at his desk he started to write one that he felt was genuine, one which was built around some neighbors who went to an old-fashioned singing school each week. He remembered a little town up on the coast of Maine he had heard his grandfather tell about; so he chose Jonesport for the setting and then by elimination of names he chose Seth Parker.

When the script was completed he persuaded a few acquaintances to rehearse it with him and a few weeks later this program was presented from a small station in New York. It was immediately successful.

Mr. Lord did not delay a moment, but taking the little money he had been able to save up, he rented a small office and started selling the scripts to radio stations throughout the country. No one had ever thought of doing this before, but before very long fifteen stations had gotten together Seth Parker casts and were presenting these weekly programs with tremendous success.

By this time rumors had spread to the National Broadcasting Company that Seth Parker was fast becoming a very popular character in radio, and so an invitation was extended to Mr. Lord to meet with the Planning Board and tell of his work. The Board usually grants about ten minutes or so for such an interview, but this time it sat for an hour and a half, laughing heartily and now and then wiping a tear as this young man fairly bubbled over with enthusiasm. The result was that he was given an opportunity to present a trial program.

The following week this same group sat for half an hour as a Seth Parker program was presented upstairs in the studio and was wired down to the Board room. It was good, they decided, very good, and then suddenly, one member spoke up and said, "That was a religious program we were listening to. Do you realize that?"

He was right, too. Mr. Lord had not presented "Seth Parker's Old Fashioned Singing School" at all, but had created an entirely new idea using the same characters as the Singing School. It was a religious program they had been listening to, but it had been so cleverly and beautifully done, they had not stopped to realize that it was anything more than just an entertaining feature.

Now the fact that it was religious may not seem like an important point to the average listener, but there are thousands and thousands of listeners to a network program, and they represent many, many creeds. What would these listeners say to a religious program in which there was plenty of humor and religion was discussed freely? It was playing with dynamite and no one realized it any better than the members of the Planning Board, but they had faith in Mr. Lord's ability and finally told him to present a meeting over the air as a test.

The best proof of the way this test was received is that, from that day to this, Mr. Lord has not even been asked to submit a script to the Broadcasting Company for approval; for he has handled this delicate problem of religion in a wonderful way. Six months after the first broadcast, a well-known New York radio critic made the statement, "I am repelled by religious services over the air and now I find I've been a devout follower of one for six months and didn't realize it was religion to which I was listening."

The program does have more religion in it now, however, than when it first started. This is because Mr. Lord has certain definite ideals, which he has developed from time to time.

He believes that religion is the result of environment; that those who are born in church-going families in most cases prefer the church of their fathers more because of convenience than because of conviction; that those who come of parents outside of church circles are not reached and the reason is that religion is too closely associated with the church. To use one of Mr. Lord's own illustrations, "The church is a good store house for religion, but you should stock up with an ample supply to take home with you."

Seth Parker believes that religion is tangible; that it is a kind word, a thoughtful deed and is not something apart from every day life.

He has probably done more to make religion a part of the American home than has any other one man.

Bits About the
Seth Parker's Hymnal Program

WHEN Phillips Lord appears before the microphone in his character of Seth Parker he bends his knees, completely changes facial expression and acts out every little detail of what he is saying.

Twelve take part in the program.

Not a soul moves during the silent prayer.

Rehearsals for the following week are held immediately after the broadcast, and on the night of the broadcast there is a two-hour rehearsal before going on the air.

The members gather in a semi-circle around the microphone and face Seth, who has a microphone of his own.

The singers are the finest obtainable, but sometimes Mr. Lord will work for a long time in order to make them forget their academic singing and do the hymns in the old fashioned way.

A real spirit of friendship has grown up among those who take part.

The organ which is heard is a genuine old time melodeon.

Lizzy in real life is the wife of Seth and they have two youngsters of whom they are very proud.

The sound of the collection is achieved by dropping match sticks into a tin cup.

Mr. Lord writes each program four times before it is finally produced.

Captain Bang's real name is Raymond Hunter. He is a church singer of long standing and a singing teacher in New York. Mr. Hunter is the original Captain Bang who was with Mr. Lord on the first evening Seth Parker was ever heard on the air.

Jane in reality is Erva Giles, who is heard in many programs over the air. She is a native of Ellsworth, Maine, which is only fifty miles from the real Jonesport.

Edward Wolters is a native of Denver, Colorado. He is occasionally heard as the Captain's brother, although in reality he is always present in the studio singing with the group.

Gertrude Foster is associated with the National Broadcasting Company. She sings alto.

Polly Robertson plays the melodeon. She played a portable melodeon over seas during the war and is familiar with the old style of playing hymns. She comes from a small southern town.

John is Richard Maxwell, who is heard on many other N. B. C. programs.

Laith is none other than Bennet Kilpack, head of the dramatic department of Brooklyn Institute. He spends much of his time in Kenebunkport, Maine.

One evening while a ten-minute rest was going on, Bennet Kilpack was telling a joke at one end of the studio, while Mr. Lord was at the other end of the studio making a few minor corrections on a script. Mr. Kilpack happened to use a rather peculiar voice in telling the story and in another minute Mr. Lord was across the room making him repeat it; for he realized here was an excellent idea for a new character. Therefore Cefus was born and is played by Mr. Kilpack.

Edward Dunham is always in the studio to be ready with the sound effects, time the program, and look after the details of production.

John Kulik, of the N. B. C., is at the control board to see that the program is modulated correctly when it comes on the air.

Four-fifths of the rehearsal time is spent in making the program homelike and natural. Nothing which is not absolutely natural is permitted to pass Mr. Lord.

The male quartet which is occasionally heard is made up of the male members of the cast who like to sing together.

Mr. Lord plays the guitar for his own accompaniments. He is also adept at the mouth organ.

The fan mail on each program ranges from 500 letters a week to 7,000. Every letter is read.

Mr. Lord always has several dollars in his pocket to use for those who are needy, as listeners occasionally send in a dollar or so to put in the collection, and Mr. Lord uses it as he encounters needy cases during the day.

LEFT TO RIGHT. FRONT ROW.

Phillips H. Lord, creator and heard as Seth Parker; Mrs. Sophia M. Lord, heard as Lizzy; Raymond Hunter, **Capt. Bang; Bennet Kilpack, heard as** Laith Pettingal and Cefus Peters; Richard Maxwell, hea d as John; Gertrude Foster, alto and a neighbor; Barbra Bruce, heard as Mother Parker; Polly Robertson, accompaniest; Edward Wolters, heard as George, the Capt.'s brother.

LEFT TO RIGHT. STANDING.

William Jordan, heard as Dr. Tanner; James Black, a neighbor; John Kulik, a neighbor; Norman Price, a neighbor; Edwin Dunham, production manager and neighbor; Erva Giles, heard as Jane.

SETH PARKER

CRITICIZING

Oft times upon a wintry eve, we'd gather at the store
Where some would play and some would talk and some would simply snore.
But when Hitch Thomas tilted back and started to advise
'Twas worth a year or two at school to hear him criticize.

He'd criticize the town and folks and touch upon the state,
And then he'd go to Washington and criticize the great.
But when he got full steam up he wasn't even awed
To go right up to heaven and criticize the Lord.

For twenty years he criticized but then there come a spell
When old Hitch Thomas shut right up and clumb within his shell.
For weeks he wouldn't say a word, but then there come a night
He tilted back his chair again and started to recite.

"Two weeks ago last Thursday night I'd say 'twas 'bout eleven,
As I was laying in my bed an angel come from heaven.
He sez, 'Now, Hitch, we've heard you talk and think you're pretty wise,
We'd like ter have yer come above and help us criticize.'

Now that's real nice I sez to him, so I put on some wings
And fluttered 'round about the room to kind of test the things.
They worked real good so off we flew and headed for the sky;
It seemed like we was headed down, we flew so awful high.

Now I ain't going to tell yer all the things I saw and done
As Peter pointed out to me the way that things was run,
But I saw proof on proof up there, that made me realize
They should have sent for me before to help them organize.

Now fust they had no government; no state or county seat,
They had no laws or anti-laws to punish them who cheat.
Why, when I showed them this and that they took down every word
And Moses got all tuckered out a-chiseling what he heard.

I criticized things right and left where I was justified,
Until I chanced to spy the Lord a-standing by my side.
He sez to me, 'Now, Hitch,' sez He, 'I've done the best I can
But I have always tried and failed to make a perfect man.

I wonder if you'd take the time to make him up for me
So I can model all the rest from one I really see.'
'Now, Lord,' I sez, 'you set down there while I work out a plan
And then I'll show you what to do to make a perfect man.'

He sat and so I started in to mix a batch of batter
From which I sifted ways of man which I thought were the matter.
I dumped a shovel full of this, and scraped up some of that,
Then next I put a pinch of lean and then a pinch of fat.

As soon as things were all mixed up I got a cup of sense
And poured in just enough conceit to give it recompense.
I put in all the things I knew to make a perfect man
And then I laid the batter in a good-sized baking pan.

A long, long time I baked that dough to give it chance to rise
So when the perfect man was done he'd be of goodly size.
I wasn't taking chances of his coming out all raw
'Cause I was out to make a man, a man without a flaw.

But when I opened up that door and saw that perfect critter
I couldn't for the life of me control an itch to titter.
I laughed at him until the tears just wouldn't let me see
And then the Lord come over there and said that man was me."

SOME VIEWS AT JONESPORT, MAINE

YOU GO TO YOUR CHURCH AND I'LL GO TO MINE

It was about five years ago that the Baptists decided to have a lobster supper and they invited Deacon Withersby, Deacon of the Methodist church, to be the guest of honor.

Well, folks stood around and talked a mite and then they started in on the supper. They'd no sooner set though before Deacon Withersby pulled some peanut butter sandwitches out of his pocket and laid them on the table.

You see, lobster didn't agree with Deacon Withersby so he'd brought along the sandwitches instead. They could have spoiled the whole supper by the Baptists arguing with the Deacon to eat lobster or he could have started the arguing by trying to get them to eat sandwitches. They didn't do it though. They all et what they had a mind to and they enjoyed it considerable.

It sort of brought out to me that what's one man's meat is another man's poison and it give me a little thought that I want to tell you about.

Now I'm not saying religion is like vittals, and yet agin it might be. I wonder perhaps if a brand of religion that's tailored for one man might not be a pretty poor fit for another.

Anyway I've got a little tune here that goes something like this.

Seth Parker's Hymnal

1 YOU GO TO YOUR CHURCH, AND I'LL GO TO MINE

SETH PARKER — PHILLIPS H. LORD

2

THE OLD RUGGED CROSS

REV. GEO. BENNARD REV. GEO. BENNARD

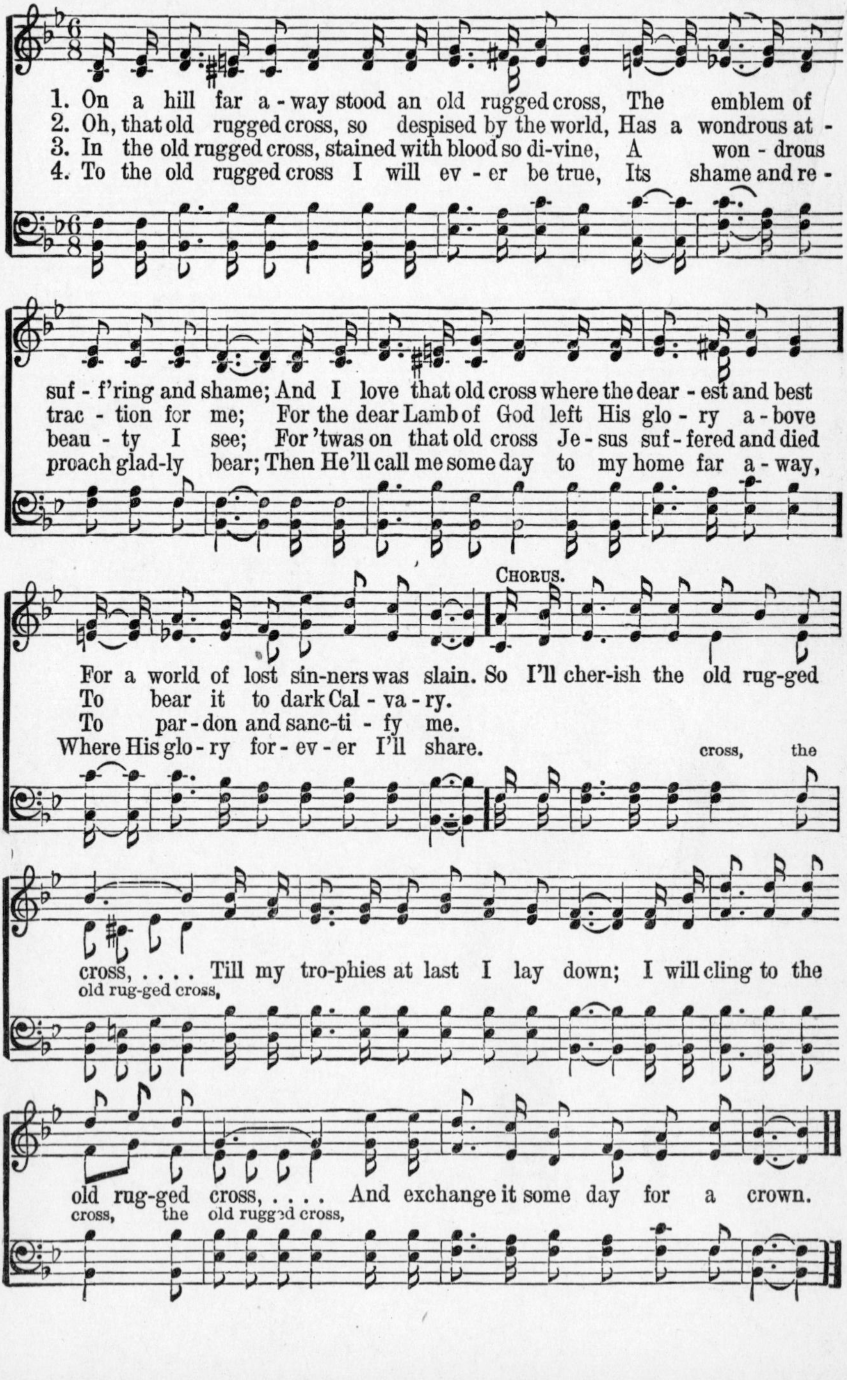

1. On a hill far a-way stood an old rugged cross, The emblem of
2. Oh, that old rugged cross, so despised by the world, Has a wondrous at-
3. In the old rugged cross, stained with blood so di-vine, A won-drous
4. To the old rugged cross I will ev-er be true, Its shame and re-

suf-f'ring and shame; And I love that old cross where the dear-est and best
trac-tion for me; For the dear Lamb of God left His glo-ry a-bove
beau-ty I see; For 'twas on that old cross Je-sus suf-fered and died
proach glad-ly bear; Then He'll call me some day to my home far a-way,

For a world of lost sin-ners was slain.
To bear it to dark Cal-va-ry.
To par-don and sanc-ti-fy me.
Where His glo-ry for-ev-er I'll share.

CHORUS.

So I'll cher-ish the old rug-ged cross, the cross, ... Till my tro-phies at last I lay down; I will cling to the old rug-ged cross, ... And exchange it some day for a crown.

(cross, the old rug-ged cross, / cross, the old rugged cross,)

3

O THAT WILL BE GLORY

C. H. G. Words and music CHAS. H. GABRIEL

1. When all my la-bors and tri-als are o'er, And I am safe on that beau-ti-ful shore, Just to be near the dear Lord I a-dore, Will thro' the a-ges be glo-ry for me. . . .
2. When, by the gift of His in-fi-nite grace, I am ac-cord-ed in heav-en a place, Just to be there and to look on His face,
3. Friends will be there I have loved long a-go; Joy like a riv-er a-round me will flow; Yet, just a smile from my Sav-ior, I know,
rit.
CHORUS. Faster.
O that will be glo-ry for me, Glo-ry for me, glo-ry for me; When by His grace I shall look on His face, That will be glo-ry, be glo-ry for me.
O................. that will be glo-ry for me, glo-ry for me, glo-ry for me;............
rit.

4 WHEN THE MISTS HAVE ROLLED AWAY

ANNIE HERBERT. Arr. IRA D. SANKEY

1. When the mists have rolled in splendor From the beau- ty of the hills, And the
2. Oft we tread the path be-fore us With a wea - ry, burdened heart; Oft we
3. We shall come with joy and gladness, We shall gath- er round the throne; Face to

sun- light falls in glad- ness On the riv - er and the rills, We re - call our
toil a- mid the shadows, And our fields are far a- part; But the Sav-iour's
face with those that love us, We shall know as we are known: And the song of

Fa - ther's prom-ise In the rain-bow of the spray: We shall know each oth- er
"Come, ye blessed" All our la - bor will re- pay, When we gath - er in the
our re-demp-tion Shall re - sound thro' end-less day When the shad-ows have de -

rit.

bet - ter When the mists have rolled a-way.
morning Where the mists have rolled a-way.
part - ed, And the mists have rolled a-way.

CHORUS

We shall know...... as we are
We shall know

known,............ Nev - er - more......... to walk a - lone,...............
as we are known, Nev - er-more to walk a- lone,

WHEN THE MISTS HAVE ROLLED AWAY

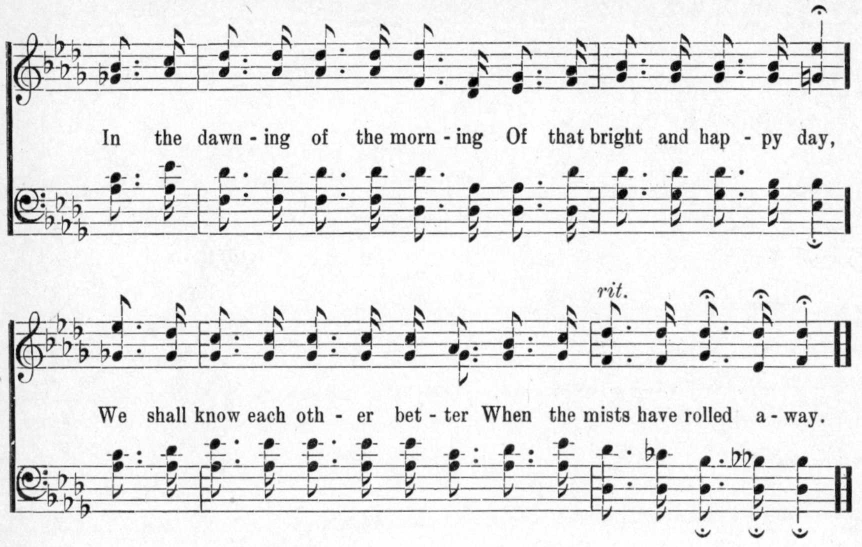

In the dawn - ing of the morn - ing Of that bright and hap - py day,
rit.
We shall know each oth - er bet - ter When the mists have rolled a - way.

5 DEAR LORD AND FATHER OF MANKIND

JOHN G. WHITTIER FREDERICK G. MAKER

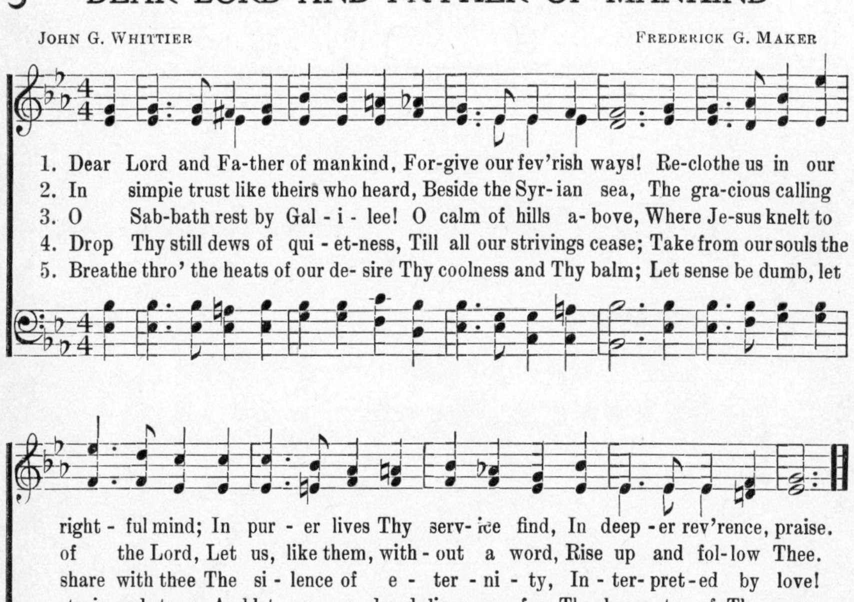

1. Dear Lord and Fa-ther of mankind, For-give our fev'rish ways! Re-clothe us in our
2. In simple trust like theirs who heard, Beside the Syr- ian sea, The gra-cious calling
3. O Sab-bath rest by Gal - i - lee! O calm of hills a- bove, Where Je-sus knelt to
4. Drop Thy still dews of qui - et-ness, Till all our strivings cease; Take from our souls the
5. Breathe thro' the heats of our de- sire Thy coolness and Thy balm; Let sense be dumb, let
right - ful mind; In pur - er lives Thy serv- ice find, In deep - er rev'rence, praise.
of the Lord, Let us, like them, with - out a word, Rise up and fol- low Thee.
share with thee The si - lence of e - ter - ni - ty, In - ter- pret - ed by love!
strain and stress, And let our or- dered lives con - fess The beau - ty of Thy peace.
flesh re-tire; Speak thro' the earthquake, wind and fire, O still small voice of calm!

JESUS IS MY NEIGHBOR

You know, I was sitting and swinging in the hammock, a couple of days ago, when some lines of the Twenty-third Psalm came to mind. The lines I was thinking about was,

"The Lord is my shepherd, I shall not want.
He maketh me to lie down in green pastures,
He leadeth me beside the still waters.
He restoreth my soul."

They're awful pretty lines to recite to yourself; and while I was reciting them I looked across the meadow, and it come to me how much more the psalm would mean if we was to have some shepherds around Jonesport, so we could see them every day.

I was sort of churning it over in my mind when all of a sudden I thought, "We haven't got any shepherds, but we have got neighbors; and wouldn't it be a pretty good idea to think of the Lord as being a neighbor?"

There's lots of things about neighbors that are just like shepherds. Shepherds have crooks they walk around with, but Sam Tuttle has one of them. The only difference between a shepherd and Sam is they hold the stick by opposite ends. The shepherd holds it so the crook is on the ground, but Sam holds the crook in his hand and calls it a cane.

The more I thought about it the more I came to see there wasn't so much difference between shepherds and neighbors anyhow; and, seeing the first cousin to a psalm is a hymn, I decided to write a little tune about it.

I don't suppose it's so much of a tune, but I'd like to have you try it over and see how you like it.

JESUS IS MY NEIGHBOR

SETH PARKER — PHILLIPS H. LORD

1. Je - sus is my neigh - bor, He lives next door to me.
2. Je - sus is my neigh - bor, He lives next door to me.
3. Come and live with Je - sus, The o - pen door stands wide.
My house is o - pen to Him, I've giv - en Him the key.
His house is al - ways o - pen, He's giv - en me the key.
You'll find the love of Je - sus, When you have stepped in - side.
We sit be - fore the fire - side, As hap - py as can be,
Since I have called up - on Him, I've real - ly come to see,
It's home for ev - 'ry wan - d'rer And rest from ev - 'ry sin,
He seems to un - der - stand me, He lives next door to me.
That Je - sus un - der - stands me, And lives next door to me.
Oh! come and live with Je - sus, You're wel - come, come right in.

7 SAVED BY GRACE

Fanny J. Crosby | George C. Stebbins

1. Some day the sil - ver cord will break, And I no more as now shall sing;
2. Some day my earth - ly house will fall, I can-not tell how soon 'twill be,
3. Some day, when fades the golden sun Beneath the ros - y - tint - ed west,
4. Some day: till then I'll watch and wait, My lamp all trimmed and burning bright,
But Oh! the joy when I shall wake With - in the pal-ace of the King!
But this I know, my All - in - all Has now a place in heav'n for me.
My blessed Lord will say, "Well done!" And I shall en - ter in - to rest.
That when my Sav - iour opes the gate, My soul to Him may take its flight.
Refrain
And I shall see Him face to face, And tell the sto-ry, saved by grace;
shall see
to face,
And I shall see Him face to face, And tell the story, saved by grace.
shall see
to face,
rit.

LEAD ME, SAVIOUR

"For thy name's sake, lead me and guide me."—Ps. 31 : 3

F. M. D.

FRANK M. DAVIS. By per.

With expression
1. Sav - iour, lead me, lest I stray, Gen - tly lead me all the way; I am safe when by Thy side, I would in Thy love a - bide (love a - bide.)
2. Thou the ref - uge of my soul, When life's storm - y bil - lows roll; I am safe when Thou art nigh, All my hopes on Thee re - ly (I re - ly).
3. Sav - iour, lead me till at last, When the storm of life is past, I shall reach the land of day, Where all tears are wiped a - way (wiped a - way).
1. Sav - iour, lead me, lest I stray, Gen - tly lead me all the way; I am safe when by Thy side, I would in Thy love a - bide.
CHORUS
Lead me, lead me, Sav - iour, lead me, lest I stray;............ Gen - tly down the stream of time, Lead me, Sav-iour, all the way.
lest I stray;
Changing stream of time,
all the way.

SAILING WITH MY FATHER

Seth Parker — Copyright, 1930, by Phillips H. Lord — Phillips H. Lord

1. I can sail the rough-est sea, If I know a-long with me
2. I will learn to nav-i-gate By temp-ta-tion's o-pen gate,
3. Though I sail the sea to-night, I'll be safe till morn-ing light
Is the guid-ing hand of my Fa-ther. Tides will have no fear for me
As I sail the seas with my Fa-ther. He has sailed the course be-fore,
In the lov-ing care of my Fa-ther. You need have no fear for me,
When I an-chor in the lea Of the lov-ing heart of my Fa-ther.
Knows where all the break-ers roar, And they hold no fear for my Fa-ther.
Though I'm on a storm-y sea; For I'll be safe with my Fa-ther.
CHORUS
A-hoy! a-hoy! a-hoy! All a-board, who are
com-ing a-board, To sail with me and my Fa-ther!

SWEET BY AND BY

S. F. Bennett J. P. Webster

1. There's a land that is fair - er than day, And by faith we can see it a - far: For the Fa - ther waits o - ver the way, To pre - pare us a dwell - ing-place there.
2. We shall sing on that beau - ti - ful shore The me - lo - di - ous songs of the blest, And our spir - its shall sor - row no more, Not a sigh for the bless - ing of rest.
3. To our boun - ti - ful Fa - ther a - bove, We will of - fer our trib - ute of praise, For the glo - ri - ous gift of His love, And the bless - ings that hal - low our days.
Chorus
In the sweet by and by,
In the sweet by and by,
We shall meet on that beau - ti - ful snore; In the
by and by;
sweet by and by,
In the sweet by and by,
We shall meet on that beau - ti - ful shore.

CALVARY

W. M'K. DARWOOD — Copyright, 1886, by Jno. R. Sweney — JNO. R. SWENEY

Moderato
1. On Calv'ry's brow .... my Sav- iour died,...............'Twas there my Lord .... was cru- ci - fied;.......... 'Twas on the cross........... He bled for me,................... And purchased there................. my par - don free.
2. 'Mid rend- ing rocks.............. and darkened skies,.............. My Sav- iour bows........... His head and dies: .... The opening veil.............. reveals the way................... To heav - en's joys.................. and end - less day.
3. O Je - sus, Lord,............ how can it be,.............That Thou shouldst give............ Thy life for me,........... To bear the cross........... and ag - o - ny, ... In that dread hour................. on Cal - va - ry?
CHORUS
O Cal - va - ry! dark Cal - va- ry! Where Je - sus shed His blood for me;
for me;
O Cal - va- ry! blest Cal - va- ry! 'Twas there my Sav-iour died for me.
rit.
p

12 I LOVE TO TELL THE STORY

KATHERINE HANKEY WILLIAM G. FISCHER

1. I love to tell the sto - ry Of un - seen things a - bove, Of Je - sus
2. I love to tell the sto - ry; More won-der - ful it seems Than all the
3. I love to tell the sto - ry; 'Tis pleas-ant to re - peat What seems each
4. I love to tell the sto - ry; For those who know it best Seem hun - ger -

and His glo - ry, Of Je - sus and His love, I love to tell the sto - ry,
gold - en fan-cies Of all our golden dreams. I love to tell the sto - ry,
time I tell it, More won-der-ful - ly sweet. I love to tell the sto - ry;
ing and thirsting To hear it like the rest. And when, in scenes of glo - ry,

Because I know 'tis true, It sat - is-fies my longings, As nothing else can do.
It did so much for me; And that is just the rea-son I tell it now to thee
For some have never heard The message of salvation From God's own holy word.
I sing the new, new song, 'Twill be the old, old story, That I have loved so long.

CHORUS

I love to tell the sto - ry! 'Twill be my theme in glo - ry

To tell the old, old sto - ry Of Je - sus and His love.

WE ARE GATHERING WITH THE LORD TODAY

I hope, if you ever come up this way, you'll stop around at the house and gather with us. I don't know of any better way to spend an evening than by just gathering together.

You know, there's lots of folks who are so busy they forget about the Lord. They turn to Him in the hour of death and sickness and sadness, and sort of get to associate Him with those things, but they forget to go to Him at other times.

If I just had a neighbor who came to me in times of trouble and when he wanted something, I think it would kind of hurt my feelings a mite. I'd want to have him ask me along on his picknicks and good times as well, and it wouldn't surprise me a whole lot if the Lord felt a good deal the same way.

Sunday evenings up here in Jonesport we just get together and have a real good time. The Lord joins in with us,—well, we wouldn't miss it for all the world.

I've always sort of cal'lated that it's a pretty poor idea to leave your religion in the racks with the hymn books, and we sort of aim to take it home with us. No cathedral was ever built so pretty that you could find the Lord in it any quicker than you could in your own home.

I've sort of got a little tune put together here that we use as an opener when we gather, and if you've got the time I'd like to have you try it over. It kind of makes a big family out of all those who are present.

13

WE ARE GATHERING WITH THE LORD TO-DAY

Copyright, 1929, by Christian Herald Co.,
Phillips H. Lord, owner
Seth Parker
Phillips H. Lord
1. We are gath'ring with the Lord to - day, We are gath'ring with the Lord to - day. We have all come to-geth-er In the good old-fash-ioned way, We are gath'ring with the Lord to - day.
2. We are gath'ring with the Lord to - day, We are gath'ring with the Lord to - day. We are going to have a meeting, And the fun has just be - gun, We are gath'ring with the Lord to - day.
3. We are gath'ring with the Lord to - day, We are gath'ring with the Lord to - day. He has come to gath - er with us, And He's al-ways going to stay, We are gath'ring with the Lord to - day.
Chorus
Won't you come, won't you come,
Won't you come, won't you come,
Won't you come and fol - low in the way? You will find some hap - py peo - ple,
Just some or - di - na - ry folks, Who are gath'ring with the Lord to - day.

O BEULAH LAND

EDGAR PAGE — JNO. R. SWENEY

1. I've reached the land of corn and wine, And all its rich-es free-ly mine;
2. My Sav-ior comes and walks with me, And sweet com-mun-ion here have we;
3. A sweet per-fume up-on the breeze Is borne from ev-er-ver-nal trees,
4. The zeph-yrs seem to float to me, Sweet sounds of Heaven's mel-o-dy,
Here shines undimmed one bliss-ful day, For all my night has passed a-way.
He gen-tly leads me by His hand, For this is Heav-en's bor-der-land.
And flow'rs, that nev-er-fad-ing grow, Where streams of life for-ev-er flow.
As an-gels with the white-robed throng Join in the sweet Re-demp-tion song.
CHORUS
O Beu-lah Land, sweet Beu-lah Land, As on thy high-est mount I stand,
I look a-way a-cross the sea, Where mansions are pre-pared for me, And
view the shin-ing glo-ry-shore,—My Heav'n, my home for-ev-er-more!

Used by permission of Mrs. Jno. R. Sweney

15 BRINGING IN THE SHEAVES

KNOWLES SHAW GEORGE A. MINOR

1. Sow-ing in the morn-ing, sow-ing seeds of kind-ness, Sow-ing in the
2. Sow-ing in the sun-shine, sow-ing in the shad-ows, Fear-ing nei-ther
3. Go-ing forth with weep-ing, sow-ing for the Mas-ter, Tho' the loss sus-
noon-tide and the dew-y eve; Wait-ing for the har-vest,
clouds nor win-ter's chill-ing breeze; By and by the har-vest,
tained our spir-it oft-en grieves; When our weep-ing's o-ver,
and the time of reap-ing, We shall come re-joic-ing, bring-ing in the sheaves.
and the la-bor end-ed, We shall come re-joic-ing, bring-ing in the sheaves.
He will bid us wel-come, We shall come re-joic-ing, bring-ing in the sheaves.
CHORUS
Bring-ing in the sheaves, bring-ing in the sheaves, We shall come re-joic-
Bring-ing in the sheaves, bring-ing in the sheaves, We shall come re-joic-
1
ing, bring-ing in the sheaves;
2
ing, bring-ing in the sheaves.

16 BRIGHTEN THE CORNER WHERE YOU ARE

INA DULEY OGDON — CHAS. H. GABRIEL

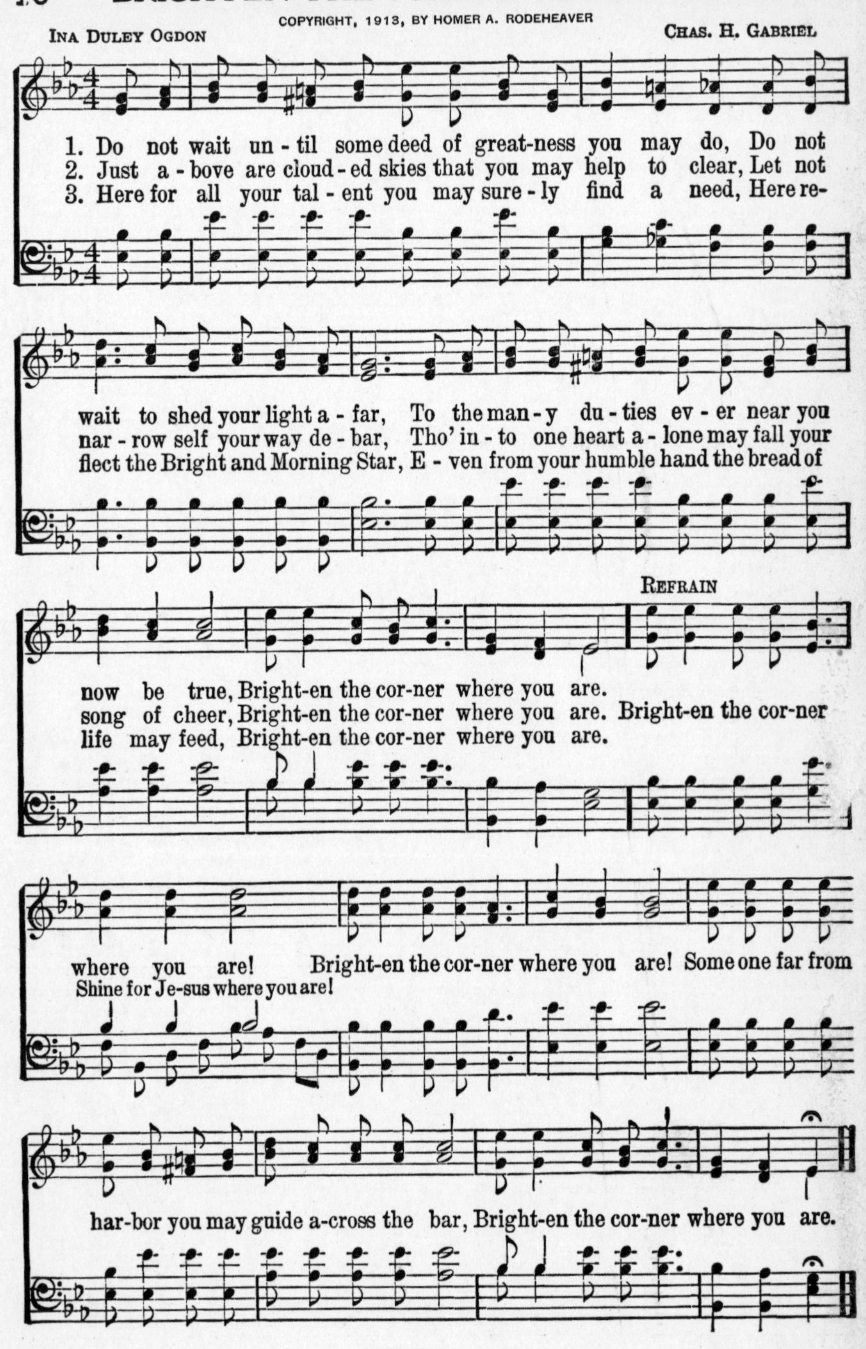
1. Do not wait un - til some deed of great-ness you may do, Do not wait to shed your light a - far, To the man-y du - ties ev - er near you now be true, Bright-en the cor-ner where you are.
2. Just a - bove are cloud - ed skies that you may help to clear, Let not nar - row self your way de - bar, Tho' in - to one heart a - lone may fall your song of cheer, Bright-en the cor-ner where you are.
3. Here for all your tal - ent you may sure - ly find a need, Here re-flect the Bright and Morning Star, E - ven from your humble hand the bread of life may feed, Bright-en the cor-ner where you are.
REFRAIN
Bright-en the cor-ner where you are!
Shine for Je-sus where you are!
Bright-en the cor-ner where you are! Some one far from har-bor you may guide a-cross the bar, Bright-en the cor-ner where you are.

17 THE NINETY AND NINE

E. C. CLEPHANE
IRA D. SANKEY
1. There were ninety and nine that safe - ly lay In the shel - ter of the fold,
2. "Lord, Thou hast here Thy ninety and nine; Are they not e - nough for Thee?"
3. But none of the ransomed ev - er knew How deep were the wa-ters cross'd;
4. "Lord, whence are those blood-drops all the way That mark out the mountain's track?"
5. But all thro' the mountains, thunder-riv'n, And up from the rock- y steep,
But one was out on the hills a- way, Far off from the gates of
But the Shepherd made an - swer: "This of mine Has wandered a - way from
Nor how dark was the night that the Lord pass'd thro' Ere He found His sheep that was
"They were shed for one who had gone a-stray Ere the Shepherd could bring him
There a - rose a great cry to the gate of heav'n, "Re - joice! I have found my
gold— A - way on the moun - tains wild and bare, A - way from the
me, And, al - though the road be rough and steep, I go to the
lost: Out in the des - ert He heard its cry— Sick and
back": "Lord, whence are Thy hands so rent and torn?" "They are pierced to-
sheep!" And the an - gels ech- oed a - round the throne, "Re- joice! for the
ten - der Shepherd's care, A - way from the ten - der Shep- herd's care.
des - ert to find my sheep, I go to the des-ert to find my sheep."
help-less, and read-y to die, Sick and helpless, and read-y to die.
night by man- y a thorn, They are pierced to- night by man-y a thorn."
Lord brings back His own! Re- joice! for the Lord brings back His own!"
rit.

HE LEADETH ME

Joseph H. Gilmore

William B. Bradbury

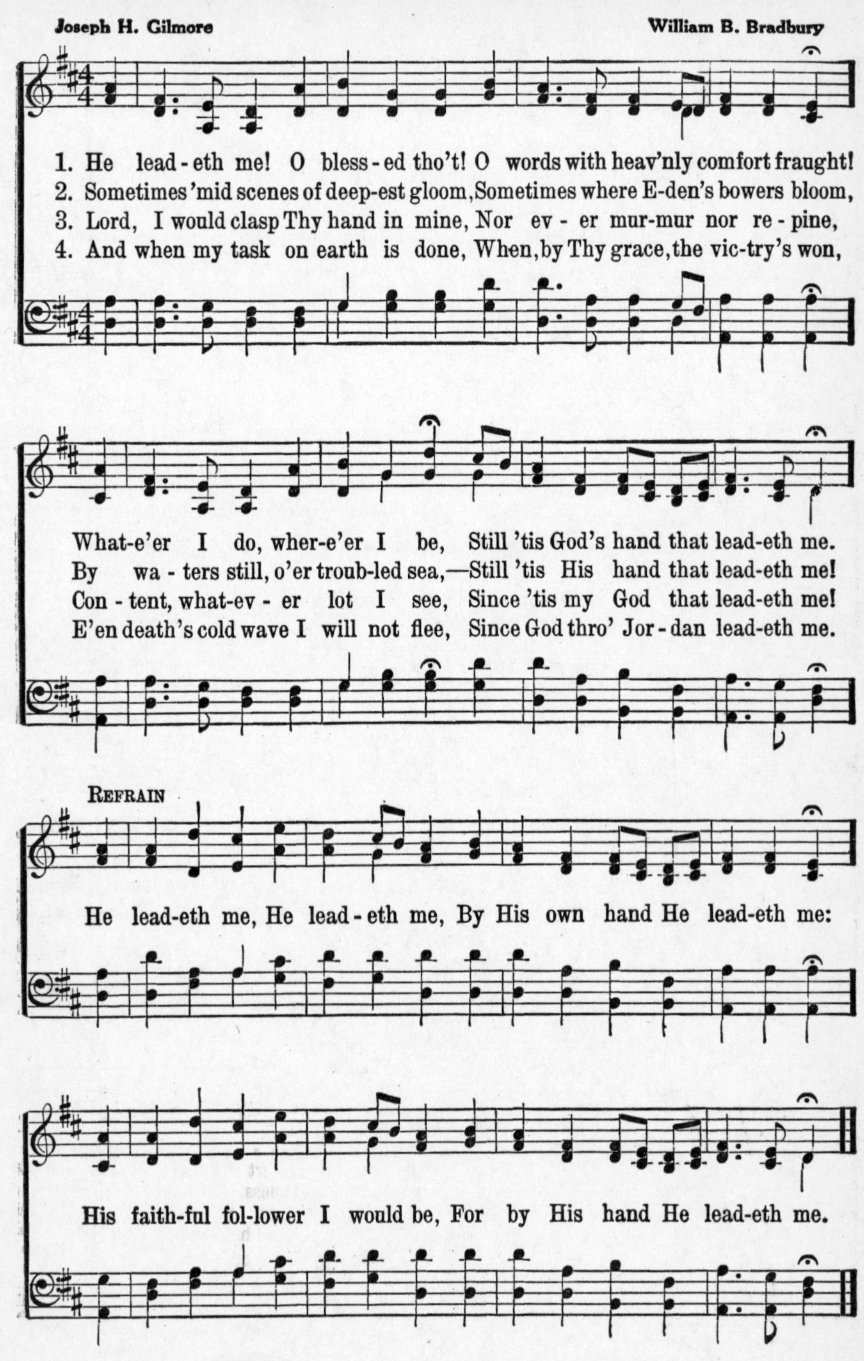
1. He lead-eth me! O bless-ed tho't! O words with heav'nly comfort fraught!
2. Sometimes 'mid scenes of deep-est gloom, Sometimes where E-den's bowers bloom,
3. Lord, I would clasp Thy hand in mine, Nor ev - er mur-mur nor re - pine,
4. And when my task on earth is done, When, by Thy grace, the vic-try's won,
What-e'er I do, wher-e'er I be, Still 'tis God's hand that lead-eth me.
By wa - ters still, o'er troub-led sea,—Still 'tis His hand that lead-eth me!
Con - tent, what-ev - er lot I see, Since 'tis my God that lead-eth me!
E'en death's cold wave I will not flee, Since God thro' Jor - dan lead-eth me.
Refrain
He lead-eth me, He lead - eth me, By His own hand He lead-eth me:
His faith-ful fol-lower I would be, For by His hand He lead-eth me.

19 THE CHURCH'S ONE FOUNDATION

Samuel J. Stone — Samuel S. Wesley

1. The Church-'s one foun - da - tion Is Je - sus Christ her Lord;
2. E - lect from ev - 'ry na - tion, Yet one o'er all the earth,
3. 'Mid toil and trib - u - la - tion, And tu - mult of her war,
4. Yet she on earth hath un - ion With God the Three in One,
She is His new cre - a - tion By wa - ter and the word:
Her char - ter of sal - va - tion, One Lord, one faith, one birth;
She waits the con - sum - ma - tion Of peace for ev - er - more;
And mys - tic sweet com - mun - ion With those whose rest is won:
From heav'n He came and sought her To be His ho - ly bride; With
One ho - ly name she bless - es, Par-takes one ho - ly food, And
Till, with the vis - ion glo - rious, Her long - ing eyes are blest, And
O hap - py ones and ho - ly! Lord, give us grace that we, Like
His own blood He bought her, And for her life He died.
to one hope she press - es, With ev - 'ry grace en - dued.
the great church vic - to - rious Shall be the church at rest.
them, the meek and low - ly, On high may dwell with Thee. A - men.

HEAVENLY JEWELS

Some years ago there used to be a traveling parson that came through Jonesport and for the whole summer he preached in the church here. He could out-orate any two other parsons I ever heard, too.

Now everybody in town used to turn out to hear him, that is everybody except Tim Brown. Tim just wouldn't go, but one time the Parson went around to see him and dared him to come for four weeks running. Tim took the dare and that's how he happened to get there.

Well, sir, the Parson set out to do extrie good and revive Tim who was sitting in the back seat. He swung his arms faster than the Widder Pease' windmill goes after she oils it. He told about the pearly gates of heaven and how the jewels sparkled and all about them.

The next week he commenced on the golden streets of heaven and how precious they were and the third week he got onto harps strung up with camel's hair, and then got onto the crowns of the angels.

After the fourth sermon he went down and got a hold of Tim before he could get out and sez to him:

"Tim, what did you think about it?"

"Well," sez Tim, "it sounded fust rate."

The Parson seen something was troubling him though, so he asked him what it was.

"I heard you tell about the golden streets," sez Tim, "and that harp playing was real interesting, too. I hope I get a chance to see the jewels up there; but honest, Parson, is that where God is?"

For four weeks the Parson had been talking about the precious jewels and the like of that, but he'd got so excited that he'd forgot to tell the big purpose of it all. He was like a little feller on Fourth of July who makes such a big noise with the shooting off of firecrackers that he forgets what the day means.

Here's a little tune that sort of goes along the same order. Perhaps you'd like to look it over.

20

HEAVENLY JEWELS

Seth Parker — Copyright, 1930, by Phillips H. Lord — Phillips H. Lord

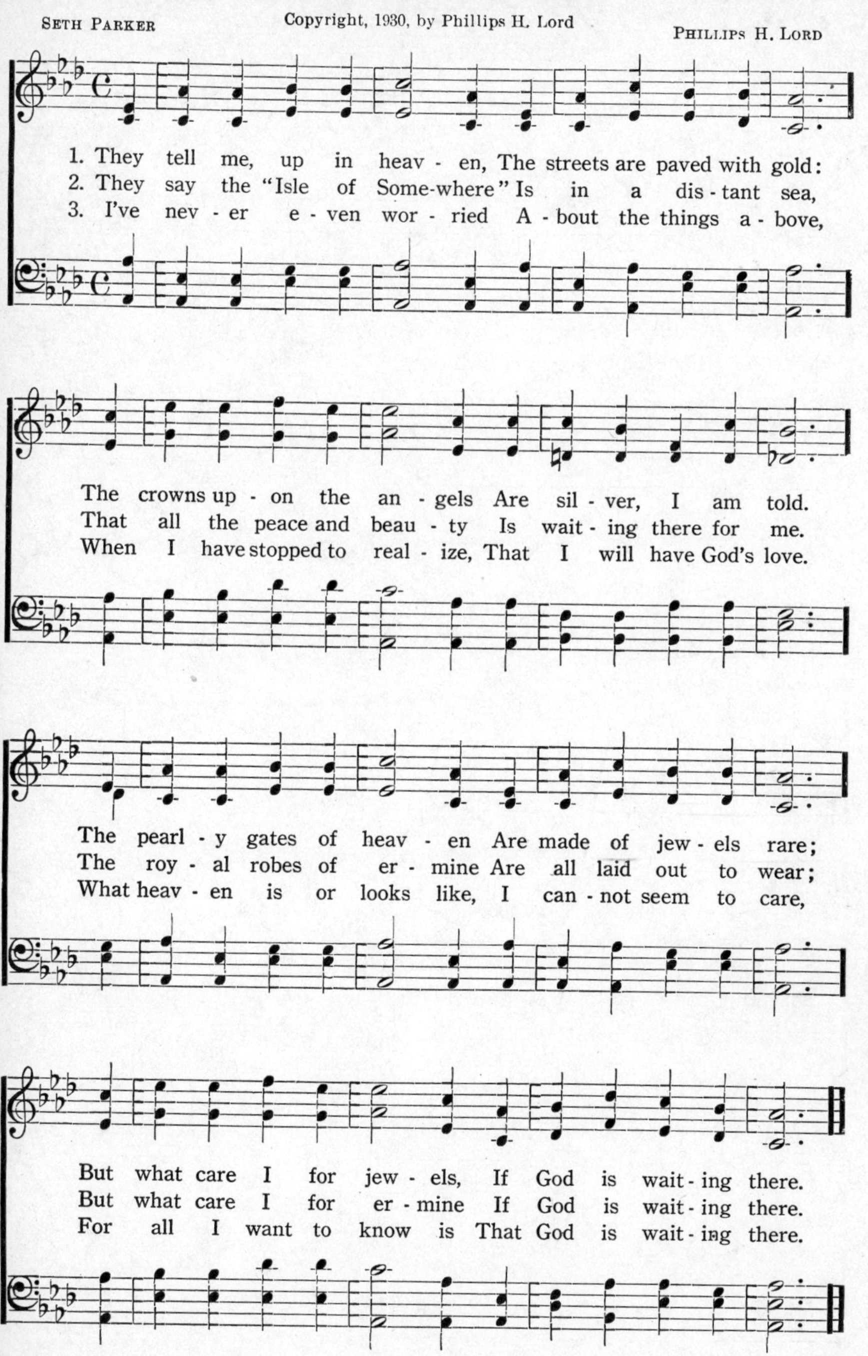
1. They tell me, up in heav - en, The streets are paved with gold:
2. They say the "Isle of Some-where" Is in a dis - tant sea,
3. I've nev - er e - ven wor - ried A - bout the things a - bove,
The crowns up - on the an - gels Are sil - ver, I am told.
That all the peace and beau - ty Is wait - ing there for me.
When I have stopped to real - ize, That I will have God's love.
The pearl - y gates of heav - en Are made of jew - els rare;
The roy - al robes of er - mine Are all laid out to wear;
What heav - en is or looks like, I can - not seem to care,
But what care I for jew - els, If God is wait - ing there.
But what care I for er - mine If God is wait - ing there.
For all I want to know is That God is wait - ing there.

21 MY FAITH LOOKS UP TO THEE
Ray Palmer
Lowell Mason
1. My faith looks up to Thee, Thou Lamb of Cal - va - ry, Sav - ior di - vine; Now hear me
2. May Thy rich grace impart Strength to my fainting heart, My zeal in-spire; As Thou hast
3. While life's dark maze I tread, And griefs around me spread, Be Thou my Guide; Bid darkness
when I pray, Take all my sin a - way, O let me from this day Be whol - ly Thine!
died for me, O may my love to Thee, Pure, warm, and changeless be,—A liv - ing fire!
turn to day, Wipe sorrow's tears a - way, Nor let me ev - er stray From Thee a - side.
22 MY JESUS, I LOVE THEE
Anonymous
A. J. Gordon
1. My Je - sus, I love Thee, I know Thou art mine, For Thee all the
2. I'll love Thee in life, I will love Thee in death, And praise Thee as
3. In mansions of glo - ry and end - less de - light, I'll ev - er a -
pleas - ures of sin I re - sign; My gra - cious Re - deem - er, my
long as Thou lend - est me breath; And say when the death-dew lies
dore Thee in heav - en so bright; I'll sing with the glit - ter - ing
Sav - ior art Thou; If ev - er I loved Thee, my Je - sus, 'tis now.
cold on my brow, If ev - er I loved Thee, my Je - sus, 'tis now.
crown on my brow, If ev - er I loved Thee, my Je - sus, 'tis now.

23 IN THE CROSS OF CHRIST

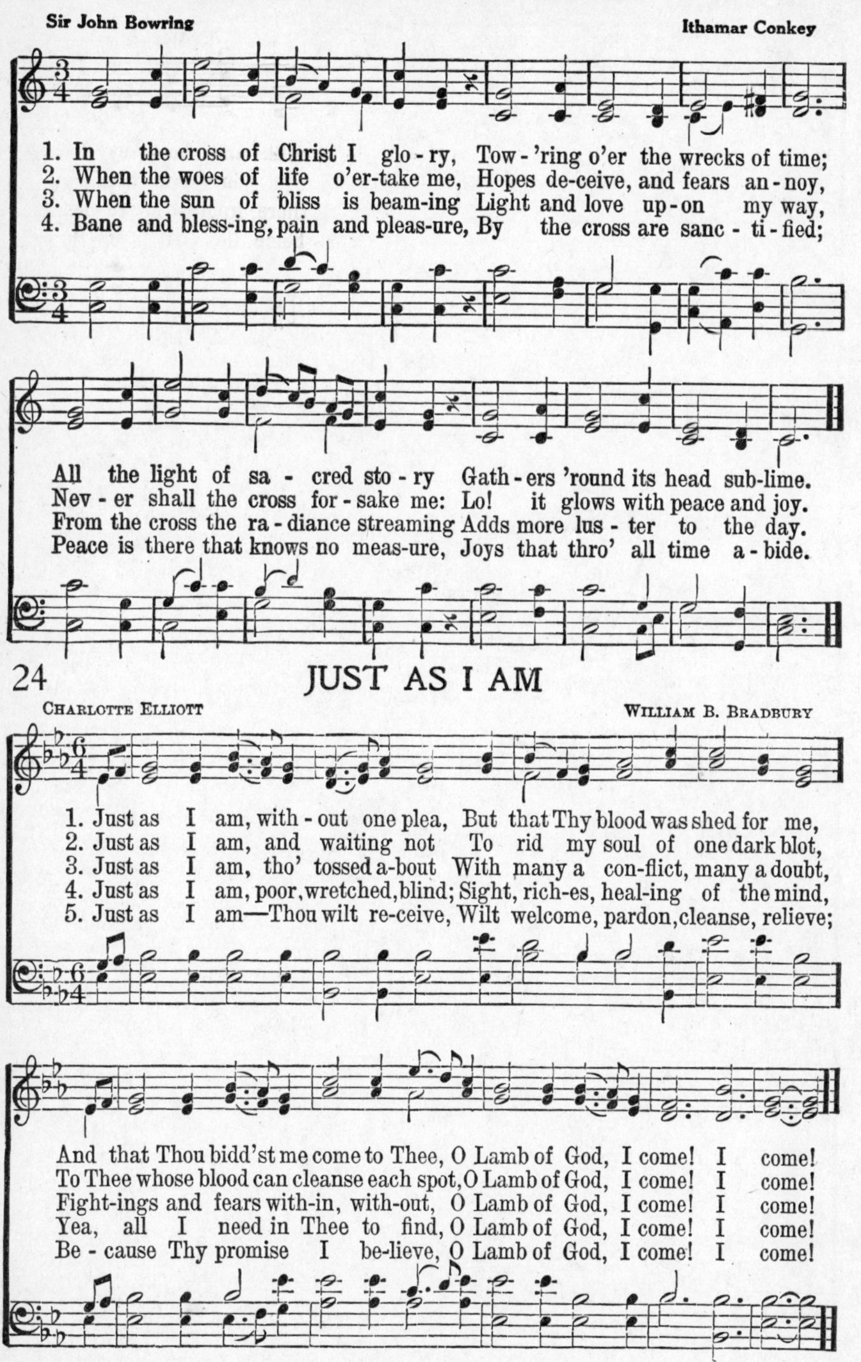
Sir John Bowring
Ithamar Conkey
1. In the cross of Christ I glo-ry, Tow-'ring o'er the wrecks of time;
2. When the woes of life o'er-take me, Hopes de-ceive, and fears an-noy,
3. When the sun of bliss is beam-ing Light and love up-on my way,
4. Bane and bless-ing, pain and pleas-ure, By the cross are sanc-ti-fied;
All the light of sa-cred sto-ry Gath-ers 'round its head sub-lime.
Nev-er shall the cross for-sake me: Lo! it glows with peace and joy.
From the cross the ra-diance streaming Adds more lus-ter to the day.
Peace is there that knows no meas-ure, Joys that thro' all time a-bide.
24
JUST AS I AM
CHARLOTTE ELLIOTT
WILLIAM B. BRADBURY
1. Just as I am, with-out one plea, But that Thy blood was shed for me,
2. Just as I am, and waiting not To rid my soul of one dark blot,
3. Just as I am, tho' tossed a-bout With many a con-flict, many a doubt,
4. Just as I am, poor, wretched, blind; Sight, rich-es, heal-ing of the mind,
5. Just as I am—Thou wilt re-ceive, Wilt welcome, pardon, cleanse, relieve;
And that Thou bidd'st me come to Thee, O Lamb of God, I come! I come!
To Thee whose blood can cleanse each spot, O Lamb of God, I come! I come!
Fight-ings and fears with-in, with-out, O Lamb of God, I come! I come!
Yea, all I need in Thee to find, O Lamb of God, I come! I come!
Be-cause Thy promise I be-lieve, O Lamb of God, I come! I come!

25

JERUSALEM THE GOLDEN

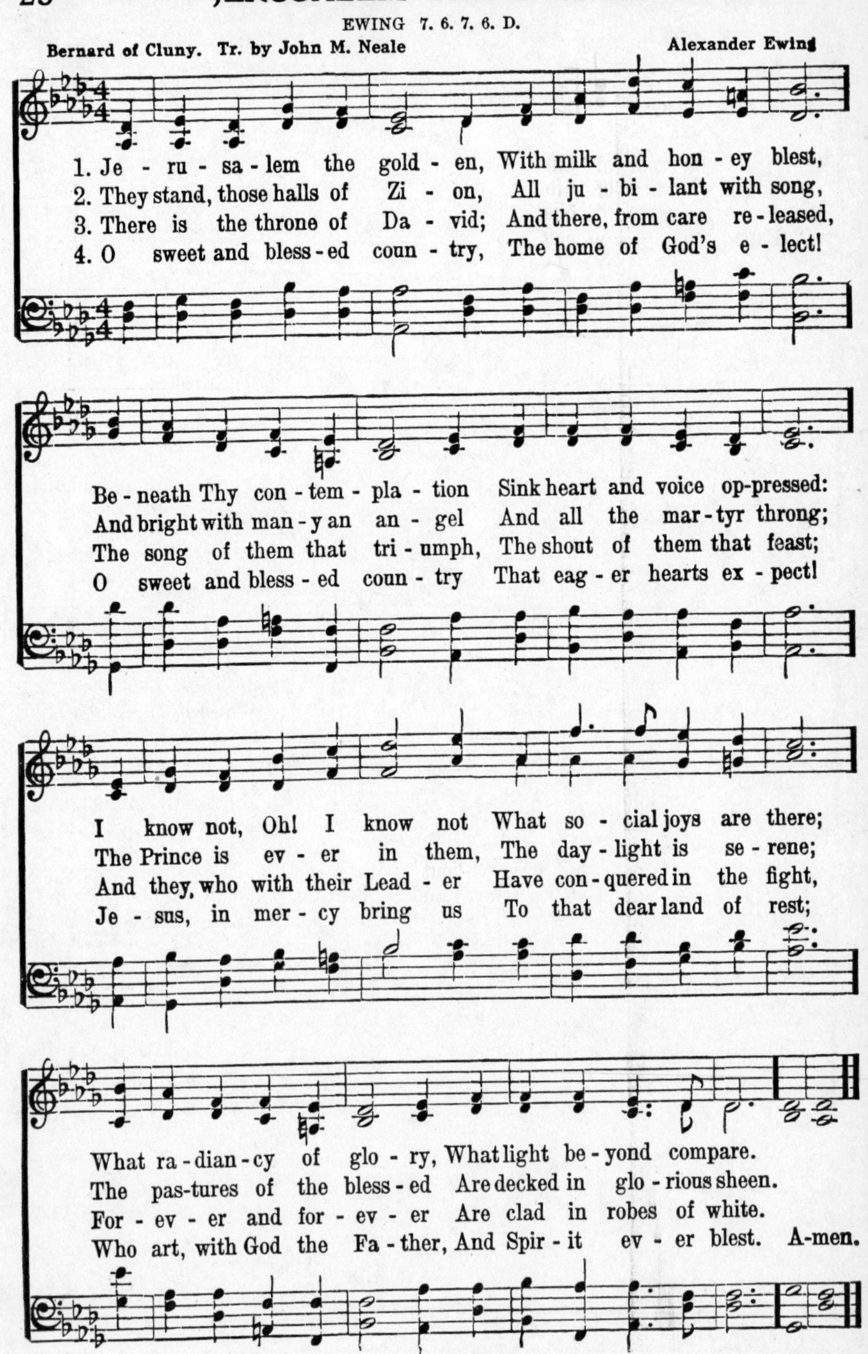
EWING 7. 6. 7. 6. D.
Bernard of Cluny. Tr. by John M. Neale
Alexander Ewing
1. Je - ru - sa - lem the gold - en, With milk and hon - ey blest,
2. They stand, those halls of Zi - on, All ju - bi - lant with song,
3. There is the throne of Da - vid; And there, from care re - leased,
4. O sweet and bless - ed coun - try, The home of God's e - lect!
Be - neath Thy con - tem - pla - tion Sink heart and voice op-pressed:
And bright with man - y an an - gel And all the mar - tyr throng;
The song of them that tri - umph, The shout of them that feast;
O sweet and bless - ed coun - try That eag - er hearts ex - pect!
I know not, Oh! I know not What so - cial joys are there;
The Prince is ev - er in them, The day - light is se - rene;
And they, who with their Lead - er Have con - quered in the fight,
Je - sus, in mer - cy bring us To that dear land of rest;
What ra - dian - cy of glo - ry, What light be - yond compare.
The pas-tures of the bless - ed Are decked in glo - rious sheen.
For - ev - er and for - ev - er Are clad in robes of white.
Who art, with God the Fa - ther, And Spir - it ev - er blest. A-men.

26 TELL ME THE OLD, OLD STORY
KATE HANKEY
Copyright property of Fanny T. Doane
W. H. DOANE
1. Tell me the Old, Old Sto - ry, Of un - seen things a - bove, Of Je - sus
2. Tell me the sto - ry slow - ly, That I may take it in— That won-der -
3. Tell me the sto - ry soft - ly, With earnest tones and grave; Re-mem-ber
4. Tell me the same old sto - ry, When you have cause to fear That this world's
and His glo - ry, Of Je - sus and His love; Tell me the sto - ry
ful re - demp-tion, God's rem - e - dy for sin; Tell me the sto - ry
I'm the sin - ner Whom Je - sus came to save; Tell me the sto - ry
emp-ty glo - ry Is cost - ing me too dear; Yes, and when that world's
sim - ply, As to a lit - tle child, For I am weak and wea - ry,
oft - en, For I for-get so soon, The "ear-ly dew" of morn-ing
al - ways If you would really be, In an - y time of troub - le,
glo - ry is dawning on my soul, Tell me the Old, Old Sto - ry:
And help - less and de - filed.
Has passed a - way at noon.
A com - fort - er to me.
"Christ Je - sus makes thee whole."
CHORUS
Tell me the Old, Old Sto - ry, Tell me the
Old, Old Sto - ry, Tell me the Old, Old Sto - ry Of Je-sus and His love,

27 MAY JESUS CHRIST BE PRAISED

From the German
Tr. by Edward Caswall

LAUDES DOMINI

Joseph Barnby

1. When morning gilds the skies, My heart awaking cries, May Jesus Christ be praised! A-like at work and prayer, To Je-sus I re-pair; May Jesus Christ be praised!
2. The night becomes as day, When from the heart we say, May Jesus Christ be praised! The pow'rs of darkness fear, When this sweet chant they hear, May Jesus Christ be praised!
3. In heav'n's e - ter-nal bliss, The loveliest strain is this, May Jesus Christ be praised! Let earth, and sea, and sky, From depth to height reply, May Jesus Christ be praised!
4. Be this, while life is mine, My can-ti - cle di-vine, May Jesus Christ be praised! Be this th' e-ter-nal song, Thro' a-ges all a - long, May Jesus Christ be praised! AMEN.

28 REJOICE, YE PURE IN HEART

Edward A. Plumtre

Arthur H. Messiter

1. Re - joice, ye pure in heart, Re - joice, give thanks and sing; Your fes - tal ban-ner wave on high,—The cross of Christ your King.
2. Bright youth and snow-crowned age, Strong men and maid-ens fair, Raise high your free, ex - ult - ing song, God's wondrous praise de - clare.
3. Yes, on through life's long path, Still chant-ing as ye go; From youth to age, by night and day, In glad-ness and in woe.
4. Still lift your stan-dard high, Still march in firm ar - ray, As war - riors thro' the dark-ness toil, Till dawns the gold - en day.

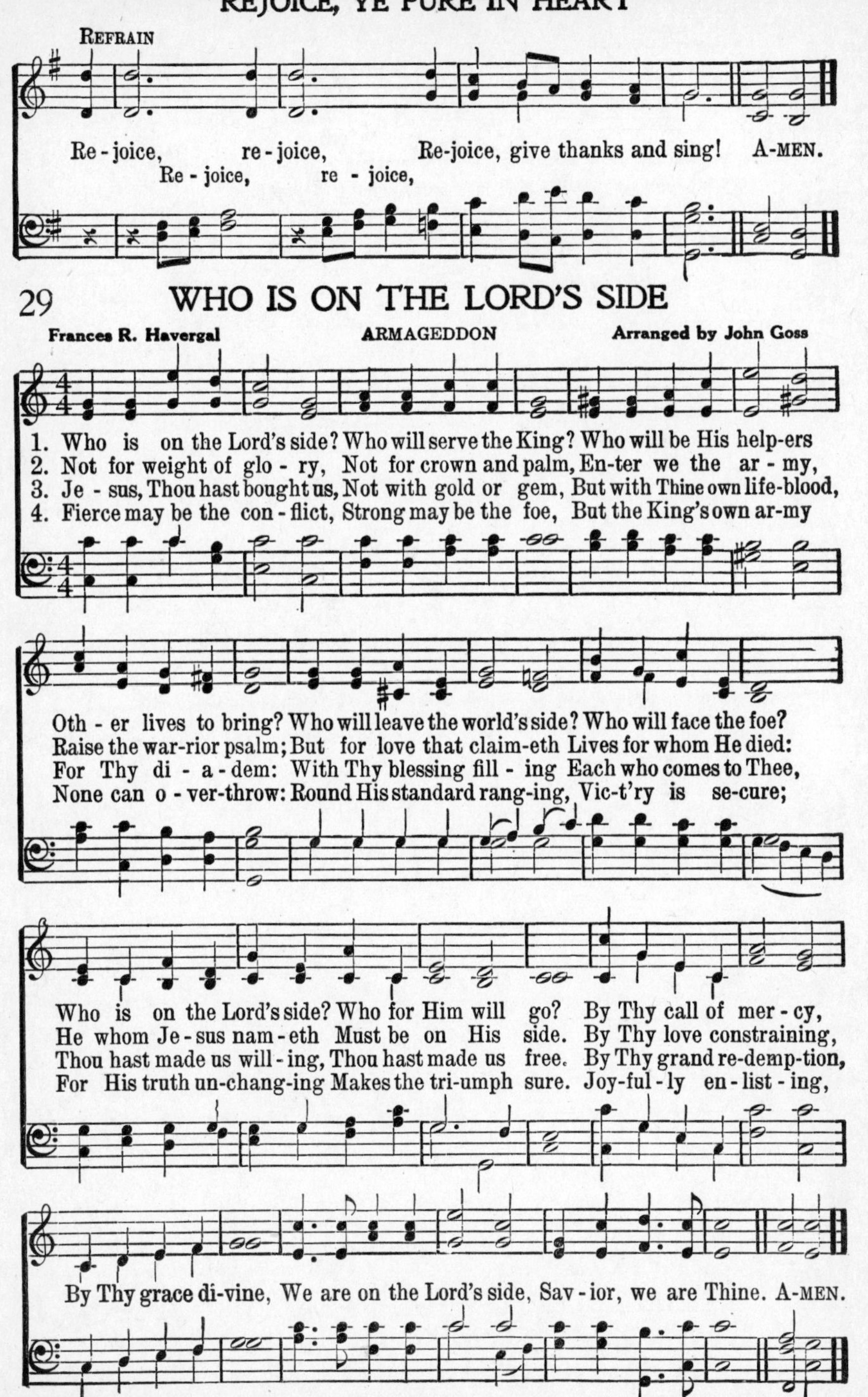
REJOICE, YE PURE IN HEART
Refrain
Re-joice, re-joice, Re-joice, give thanks and sing! A-men.
Re-joice, re-joice,
29 WHO IS ON THE LORD'S SIDE
Frances R. Havergal
ARMAGEDDON
Arranged by John Goss
1. Who is on the Lord's side? Who will serve the King? Who will be His help-ers
2. Not for weight of glo-ry, Not for crown and palm, En-ter we the ar-my,
3. Je-sus, Thou hast bought us, Not with gold or gem, But with Thine own life-blood,
4. Fierce may be the con-flict, Strong may be the foe, But the King's own ar-my
Oth-er lives to bring? Who will leave the world's side? Who will face the foe?
Raise the war-rior psalm; But for love that claim-eth Lives for whom He died:
For Thy di-a-dem: With Thy blessing fill-ing Each who comes to Thee,
None can o-ver-throw: Round His standard rang-ing, Vic-t'ry is se-cure;
Who is on the Lord's side? Who for Him will go? By Thy call of mer-cy,
He whom Je-sus nam-eth Must be on His side. By Thy love constraining,
Thou hast made us will-ing, Thou hast made us free. By Thy grand re-demp-tion,
For His truth un-chang-ing Makes the tri-umph sure. Joy-ful-ly en-list-ing,
By Thy grace di-vine, We are on the Lord's side, Sav-ior, we are Thine. A-men.

THE OLD-FASHIONED FAITH

Rev. N. A. McAulay

B. D. Ackley

1. I am somewhat old-fashioned, I know, When it comes to re-lig-ion and God;
2. I be-lieve that the Bi-ble is true, Tho' the crit-ics have torn it a-part,
3. I be-lieve our re-lig-ion must be Not a cloak for our meanness or shame,
Man-y think I am pain-ful-ly slow Since I walk where my fathers have trod.
All its warnings and mir-a-cles, too, I do whol-ly ac-cept with my heart.
But a pow-er from bondage to free All who trust in that heav-en-ly name.
I be-lieve in repentance from sin, And that Je-sus with-in us must dwell;
I be-lieve that the Sabbath was made To be sa-cred-ly kept for the Lord;
I am tell-ing the peo-ple each day, That the sin-ner for-ev-er is lost,
I be-lieve that if heav-en we win, We must flee from the ter-rors of hell.
And when broken for pleasure or trade We shall miss the e-ter-nal re-ward.
Who has failed to ac-cept the true way Which has o-pened at in-fi-nite cost.
Chorus
I'm a lit-tle old-fashioned, I know; But God's peace has a home in my soul,

THE OLD-FASHIONED FAITH

31 SHALL WE MEET?

H. L. Hastings — Elihu S. Rice

And I'll praise Him, wher-ev - er I go, For cleansing and making me whole.
1. Shall we meet be-yond the riv - er, Where the surg - es cease to roll,
2. Shall we meet be-yond the riv - er, When our storm - y voyage is o'er?
3. Shall we meet in yon - der cit - y, Where the tow'rs of crys - tal shine,
4. Shall we meet there many a loved one That was torn from our em - brace?
5. Shall we meet with Christ our Sav - ior, When He comes to claim His own?
Where in all the bright for - ev - er, Sor - row ne'er shall press the soul?
Shall we meet and cast the an - chor By the bright ce - les - tial shore?
Where the walls are all of jas - per, Built by work - man-ship di - vine?
Shall we lis - ten to their voic - es, And be - hold them face to face?
Shall we know His bless - ed fa - vor, And sit down up - on His throne?
Refrain
Shall we meet, shall we meet, Shall we meet be-yond the riv - er?
Shall we meet be - yond the riv - er, Where the surg - es cease to roll?

32 O JESUS, I HAVE PROMISED

John E. Bode — Arthur H. Mann

1. O Je-sus, I have promised To serve Thee to the end; Be Thou for-ev - er
2. O let me feel Thee near me, The world is ev - er near; I see the sights that
3. O Jesus, Thou hast promised To all who fol-low Thee That where Thou art in
near me, My Mas-ter and my Friend: I shall not fear the bat - tle If Thou art
dazzle, The tempting sounds I hear: My foes are ev - er near me, Around me
glo - ry There shall Thy servant be; And, Je - sus, I have promised To serve Thee
by my side, Nor wan-der from the path - way If Thou wilt be my Guide.
and with - in; But, Je - sus, draw Thou nearer, And shield my soul from sin.
to the end; O give me grace to fol - low My Mas - ter and my Friend.
33 TAKE MY LIFE, AND LET IT BE
Frances R. Havergal
C. H. A. Malan
1. Take my life, and let it be Con-se - cra - ted, Lord, to Thee; Take my hands, and
2. Take my feet, and let them be Swift and beau-ti - ful for Thee; Take my voice, and
3. Take my sil - ver and my gold, Not a mite would I with-hold; Take my mo-ments
4. Take my will and make it Thine, It shall be no lon-ger mine; Take my heart, it

TAKE MY LIFE, AND LET IT BE
let them move At the im-pulse of Thy love, At the im-pulse of Thy love.
let me sing Al-ways, on - ly, for my King, Al-ways, on-ly, for my King.
and my days, Let them flow in cease-less praise, Let them flow in ceaseless praise.
is Thine own, It shall be Thy roy - al throne, It shall be Thy roy - al throne.
34 HAVE THINE OWN WAY, LORD
A. A. P.
COPYRIGHT, 1907, RENEWAL. HOPE PUB. CO., OWNERS
GEO. C. STEBBINS
Slowly
1. Have Thine own way, Lord! Have Thine own way! Thou art the
2. Have Thine own way, Lord! Have Thine own way! Search me and
3. Have Thine own way, Lord! Have Thine own way! Wound-ed and
4. Have Thine own way, Lord! Have Thine own way! Hold o'er my
Pot - ter; I am the clay Mould me and make me Aft - er Thy
try me, Mas-ter, to - day! Whit - er than snow, Lord, Wash me just
wea - ry, Help me, I pray! Pow - er—all pow - er—Sure-ly is
be - ing Ab-so-lute sway! Fill with Thy Spir - it Till all shall
will, While I am wait - ing, Yield - ed and still.
now, As in Thy pres - ence Hum - bly I bow.
Thine! Touch me and heal me, Sav - ior di - vine!
see. Christ on - ly, al - ways, Liv - ing in me!

35

IF YOU'RE HAPPY

(THE LORD IS HAPPY, TOO)

SETH PARKER — Copyright, 1930, by Phillips H. Lord — Phillips H. LORD

1. If you think that the Lord is gloom - y, If you think that the
2. You will find that the Lord is hap - py, If He thinks you are
Lord is blue, You will find that you've been mis - tak - en; It
hap - py, too. You are apt to find Him feel - ing The
is - n't the Lord, it's you. You've gone to the Lord with trou - ble,
ver - y same as He finds you. But, if the Lord had His way,
You have gone to the Lord when sad. Just change things 'round the
You would sel - dom find Him sad. He'll un - der - stand your
CHORUS
next time, And go to the Lord when you're glad.
sor - row, But wants you, too, when you're glad.
When you're happy, the

IF YOU'RE HAPPY
1532326
Lord is hap - py, too; When you're smil- ing, the Lord will smile at you.
Don't you think it's fair when all is said To vis - it the Lord be -
fore you're dead. When you're laugh - ing, the Lord will un - der- stand
'Cause He made laughs, the same as He made man; And if
you should think the Lord is sad, Try call - ing on Him when you're glad.

YIELD NOT TO TEMPTATION

H. R. P. Dr. H. R. Palmer

1. Yield not to temp-ta - tion, For yield-ing is sin; Each vic - t'ry will
2. Shun e - vil com-pan-ions, Bad lan-guage dis - dain; God's name hold in
3. To him that o'er-com-eth, God giv - eth a crown; Thro' faith we will
help you Some oth - er to win; Fight man-ful - ly on - ward,
rev-'rence, Nor take it in vain; Be thought-ful and ear - nest,
con - quer, Tho' oft - en cast down; He who is our Sav - ior,
Dark pas-sions sub - due; Look ev - er to Je - sus, He'll car-ry you through.
Kind-heart-ed and true; Look ev - er to Je - sus, He'll car-ry you through.
Our strength will re - new; Look ev - er to Je - sus, He'll car-ry you through.
Chorus
Ask the Sav - ior to help you, Com-fort, strength-en, and keep you;
He is will - ing to aid you, He will car - ry you through.

37

I AM COMING HOME

A. H. ACKLEY — B. D. ACKLEY

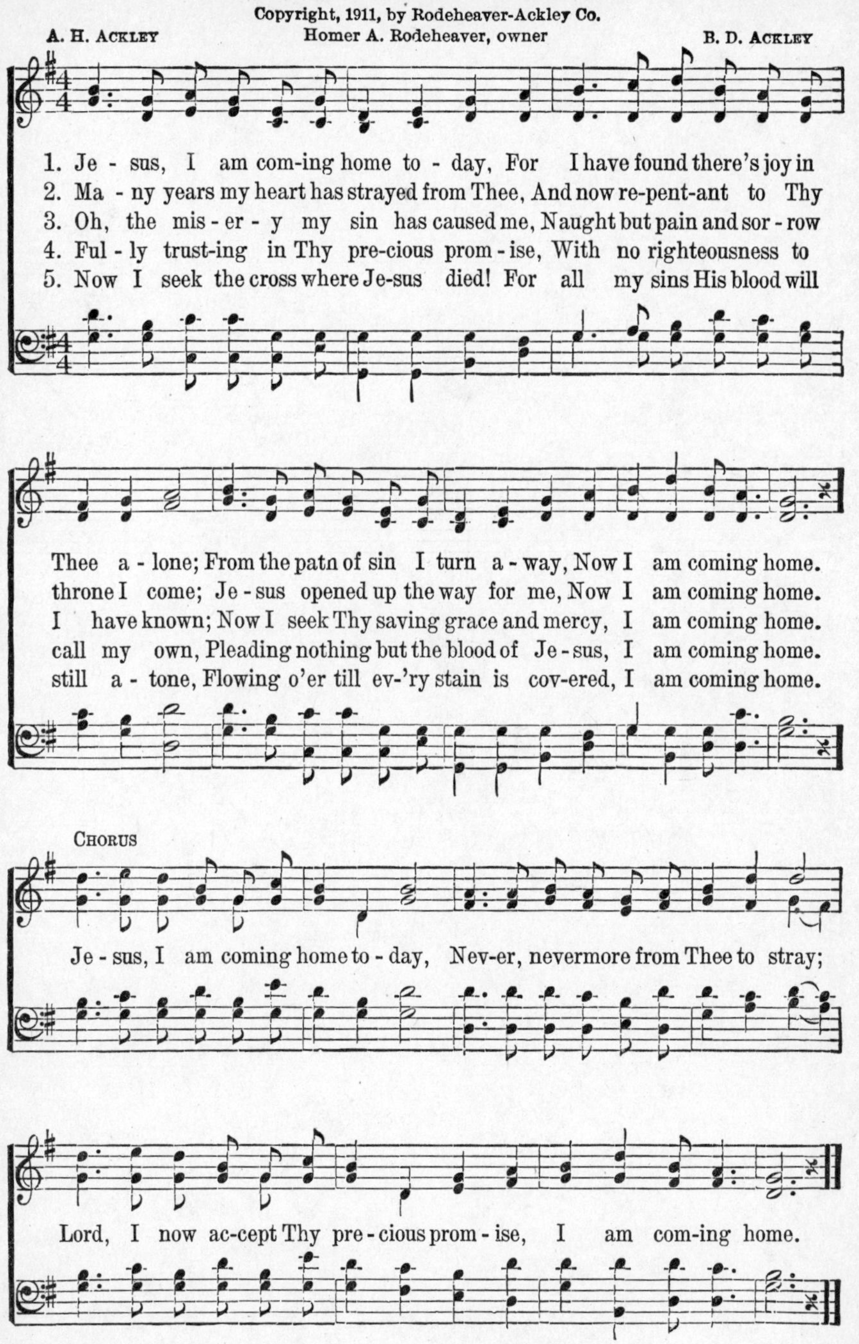
1. Je - sus, I am com-ing home to - day, For I have found there's joy in Thee a - lone; From the path of sin I turn a - way, Now I am coming home.
2. Ma - ny years my heart has strayed from Thee, And now re-pent-ant to Thy throne I come; Je - sus opened up the way for me, Now I am coming home.
3. Oh, the mis - er - y my sin has caused me, Naught but pain and sor - row I have known; Now I seek Thy saving grace and mercy, I am coming home.
4. Ful - ly trust-ing in Thy pre-cious prom - ise, With no righteousness to call my own, Pleading nothing but the blood of Je - sus, I am coming home.
5. Now I seek the cross where Je-sus died! For all my sins His blood will still a - tone, Flowing o'er till ev-'ry stain is cov-ered, I am coming home.
CHORUS
Je - sus, I am coming home to - day, Nev-er, nevermore from Thee to stray;
Lord, I now ac-cept Thy pre - cious prom - ise, I am com-ing home.

SWEETER AS THE YEARS GO BY

COPYRIGHT, 1912, BY CHAS. H. GABRIEL
HOMER A. RODEHEAVER, OWNER
Mrs. C. H. M.
Mrs. C. H. Morris
1. Of Je-sus' love that sought me, When I was lost in sin; Of won-drous
2. He trod in old Ju-de-a Life's pathway long a-go; The peo-ple
3. 'Twas wondrous love which led Him For us to suf-fer loss— To bear with-
grace that brought me Back to His fold a-gain; Of heights and depths of
thronged a-bout Him, His sav-ing grace to know; He healed the bro-ken-
out a mur-mur, The an-guish of the cross; With saints redeemed in
mer-cy, Far deep-er than the sea, And high-er than the heaven's, My
heart-ed, And caused the blind to see; And still His great heart yearneth In
glo-ry, Let us our voic-es raise, Till heav'n and earth re-ech-o With
theme shall ev-er be.
love for e-ven me.
our Redeemer's praise.
CHORUS
Sweet-er as the years go by, ...
Sweet - er as the years go by, 'Tis
Sweet-er as the years go by; Rich-er, full-er, deep-er,
sweet - er as the years go by;

SWEETER AS THE YEARS GO BY

39 I LOVE HIM

rit.
Je - sus' love is sweet - er, Sweet - er as the years go by.
London Hymn Book
Stephen C Foster
1. Gone from my heart the world and all its charms; Now thro' the blood I'm saved from all a-larms; Down at the cross my heart is bending low; The pre-cious blood of Je - sus cleanses white as snow.
2. Once I was lost, and 'way down deep in sin; Once was a slave to pas-sions fierce with-in; Once was a - fraid to meet an an - gry God, But now I'm cleansed from ev'ry stain thro' Jesus' blood.
3. Once I was bound, but now I am set free; Once I was blind, but now the light I see; Once I was dead, but now in Christ I live, To tell the world around the peace that He doth give.
Chorus.
I love Him, I love Him, Because He first loved me, And purchased my sal-va-tion on Cal-v'ry's tree.

40 DAY IS DYING IN THE WEST

Mary A. Lathbury — William F. Sherwin

1. Day is dy - ing in the west, Heav'n is touching earth with rest; Wait and
2. Lord of life, beneath the dome Of the u - ni-verse, Thy home, Gath-er
3. While the deep'ning shadows fall, Heart of Love, en - fold-ing all, Thro' the
4. When for - ev - er from our sight Pass the stars, the day, the night, Lord of

worship while the night Sets her ev-'ning lamps alight Thro' all the sky.
us, who seek Thy face, To the fold of Thy embrace, For Thou art nigh.
glo - ry and the grace Of the stars that veil Thy face, Our hearts as - cend.
an - gels, on our eyes Let e - ter-nal morning rise, And shadows end!

Refrain

Ho - ly, ho - ly, ho - ly, Lord God of Hosts! Heav'n and earth are full of

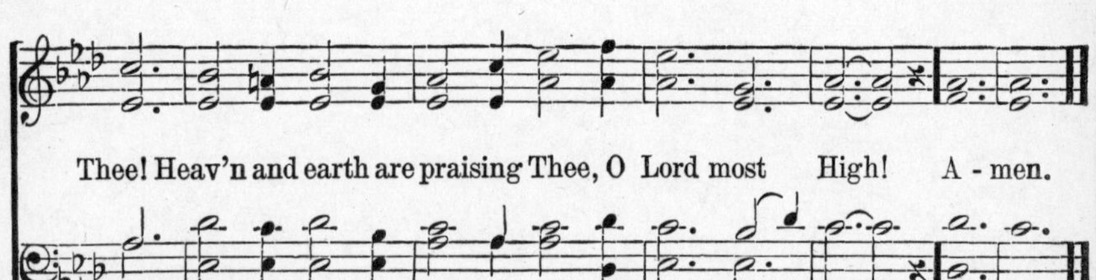
Thee! Heav'n and earth are praising Thee, O Lord most High! A - men.

41
LOVE DIVINE
CHARLES WESLEY
JOHN ZUNDEL
1. Love di - vine, all love ex - cel - ling, Joy of heav'n to earth come down!
2. Breathe, O breathe Thy lov-ing Spir - it In - to ev - 'ry troub-led breast!
3. Come, Al-might - y to de - liv - er, Let us all Thy life re - ceive;
4. Fin - ish then Thy new cre - a - tion; Pure and spot-less let us be;
Fix in us Thy hum - ble dwelling; All Thy faith-ful mer - cies crown.
Let us all in Thee in - her - it, Let us find that sec - ond rest.
Sud-den - ly re - turn, and nev - er, Nev - er - more Thy tem - ples leave:
Let us see Thy great sal - va - tion, Per - fect - ly re-stored in Thee:
Je - sus, Thou art all com-pas-sion, Pure, un-bound-ed love Thou art;
Take a - way our bent to sin - ning, Al - pha and O - me - ga be;
Thee we would be al - ways blessing, Serve Thee as Thy hosts a - bove,
Changed from glo-ry in - to glo - ry, Till in heav'n we take our place,
Vis - it us with Thy sal - va - tion; En - ter ev - 'ry trem-bling heart.
End of faith, as its be - gin-ning, Set our hearts at lib - er - ty.
Pray, and praise Thee with-out ceas - ing, Glo - ry in Thy per - fect love.
Till we cast our crowns be-fore Thee, Lost in won - der, love and praise.

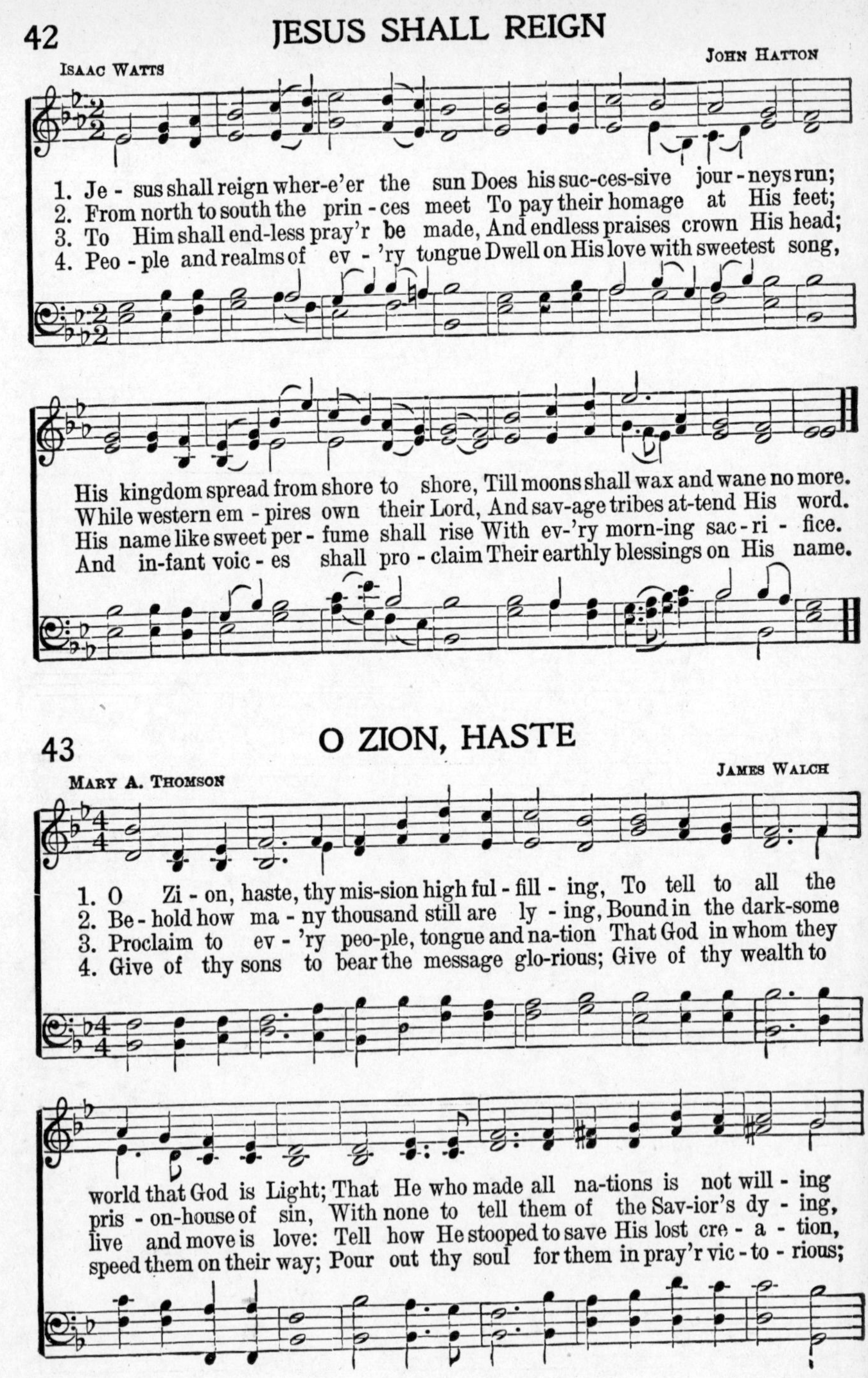
42
JESUS SHALL REIGN
ISAAC WATTS
JOHN HATTON
1. Je - sus shall reign wher-e'er the sun Does his suc-ces-sive jour - neys run;
2. From north to south the prin - ces meet To pay their homage at His feet;
3. To Him shall end-less pray'r be made, And endless praises crown His head;
4. Peo - ple and realms of ev - 'ry tongue Dwell on His love with sweetest song,
His kingdom spread from shore to shore, Till moons shall wax and wane no more.
While western em - pires own their Lord, And sav-age tribes at-tend His word.
His name like sweet per - fume shall rise With ev-'ry morn-ing sac - ri - fice.
And in-fant voic - es shall pro - claim Their earthly blessings on His name.
43
O ZION, HASTE
MARY A. THOMSON
JAMES WALCH
1. O Zi - on, haste, thy mis-sion high ful - fill - ing, To tell to all the
2. Be - hold how ma - ny thousand still are ly - ing, Bound in the dark-some
3. Proclaim to ev - 'ry peo-ple, tongue and na-tion That God in whom they
4. Give of thy sons to bear the message glo-rious; Give of thy wealth to
world that God is Light; That He who made all na-tions is not will - ing
pris - on-house of sin, With none to tell them of the Sav-ior's dy - ing,
live and move is love: Tell how He stooped to save His lost cre - a - tion,
speed them on their way; Pour out thy soul for them in pray'r vic - to - rious;

O ZION, HASTE

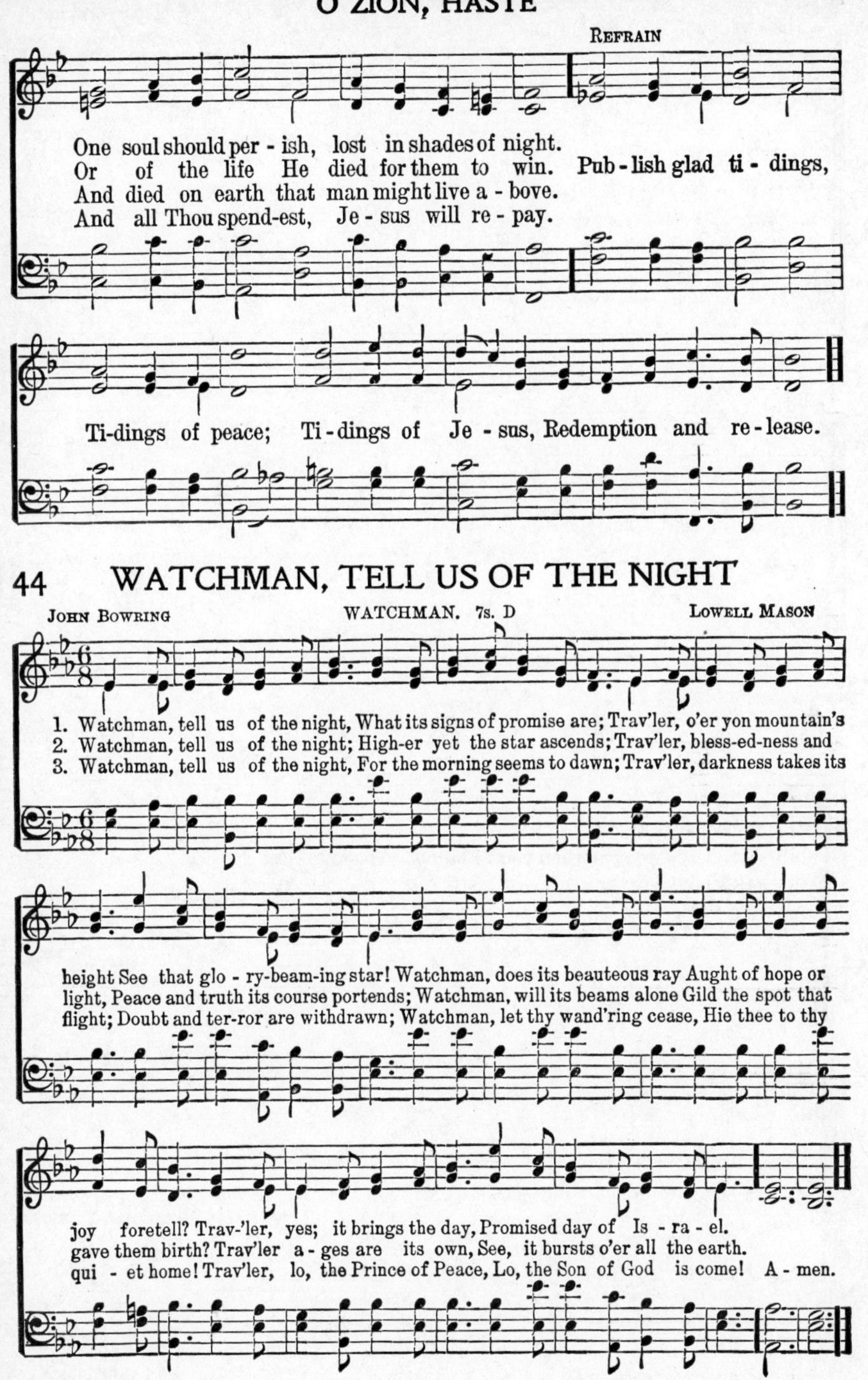
REFRAIN
One soul should per - ish, lost in shades of night.
Or of the life He died for them to win. Pub - lish glad ti - dings,
And died on earth that man might live a - bove.
And all Thou spend-est, Je - sus will re - pay.
Ti-dings of peace; Ti - dings of Je - sus, Redemption and re - lease.
44 WATCHMAN, TELL US OF THE NIGHT
JOHN BOWRING
WATCHMAN. 7s. D
LOWELL MASON
1. Watchman, tell us of the night, What its signs of promise are; Trav'ler, o'er yon mountain's
2. Watchman, tell us of the night; High-er yet the star ascends; Trav'ler, bless-ed-ness and
3. Watchman, tell us of the night, For the morning seems to dawn; Trav'ler, darkness takes its
height See that glo - ry-beam-ing star! Watchman, does its beauteous ray Aught of hope or
light, Peace and truth its course portends; Watchman, will its beams alone Gild the spot that
flight; Doubt and ter-ror are withdrawn; Watchman, let thy wand'ring cease, Hie thee to thy
joy foretell? Trav-'ler, yes; it brings the day, Promised day of Is - ra - el.
gave them birth? Trav'ler a - ges are its own, See, it bursts o'er all the earth.
qui - et home! Trav'ler, lo, the Prince of Peace, Lo, the Son of God is come! A - men.

45 SOMEBODY CARES

FANNIE EDNA STAFFORD — HOMER A. RODEHEAVER

1. Some-bod - y knows when your heart aches, And ev'rything seems to go wrong;
2. Some-bod - y cares when you're tempted, And your mind grows dizzy and dim;
3. Some-bod - y loves you when wea - ry; Somebody loves you when strong;

Some-bod - y knows when the shadows Need chasing a - way with a song;
Some-bod - y cares when you're weakest, And farthest a - way from Him;
Al - ways is wait - ing to help you, He watches you—one of the throng

Some-bod - y knows when you're lonely, Tir - ed, dis-cour-aged and blue;
Some-bod - y grieves when you're fallen, You are not lost from His sight;
Need-ing His friendship so ho - ly, Need-ing His watch-care so true;

Some-bod-y wants you to know Him, And know that He dear - ly loves you.
Some-bod-y waits for your com - ing, And He'll drive the gloom from your night.
His name? We call His name Je - sus; He loves ev - 'ry - one, He loves you.

46 MOTHER'S PRAYERS HAVE FOLLOWED ME

COPYRIGHT, 1912, BY B. D. ACKLEY
HOMER A. RODEHEAVER, OWNER
Lizzie DeArmond.
B. D. Ackley
1. I grieved my Lord from day to day, I scorned His love so full and free, And though I wandered far away, My mother's pray'rs have followed me.
2. O'er desert wild, o'er mountain high A wanderer I chose to be, A wretched soul condemned to die, Still mother's
3. He turned my darkness into light, This blessed Christ of Calvary, I'll praise His name both day and night, That mother's
Refrain.
I'm coming home, I'm coming home, To live my wasted life anew, For mother's pray'rs have followed me, Have followed me the whole world thro'.

47 O HAPPY DAY
PHILIP DODDRIDGE
E. F. RIMBAULT
1. { O hap-py day that fixed my choice On Thee, my Sav-ior and my God!
Well may this glow-ing heart re-joice, And tell its rap-tures all a-broad. }
2. { O hap-py bond, that seals my vows To Him who mer-its all my love!
Let cheerful an-thems fill His house, While to that sa-cred shrine I move. }
3. { 'Tis done: the great transaction's done; I am my Lord's and He is mine;
He drew me, and I followed on, Charmed to con-fess the voice di-vine. }
4. { Now rest, my long-di-vid-ed heart; Fixed on this bliss-ful cen-tre, rest;
Nor ev-er from my Lord de-part, With Him of ev-'ry good possessed. }
FINE
Hap-py day, hap-py day, When Je-sus washed my sins a-way!
D. S.
He taught me how to watch and pray, And live re-joic-ing ev-'ry day;
48 CLOSE TO THEE
FANNY J. CROSBY
SILAS J. VAIL
1. Thou, my ev-er-last-ing por-tion, More than friend or life to me;
2. Not for ease or world-ly pleas-ure, Nor for fame my pray'r shall be;
3. Lead me through the vale of shad-ows, Bear me o'er life's fit-ful sea;
FINE
D.S.-All a-long my pil-grim jour-ney Sav-ior, let me walk with Thee.
D.S.-Glad-ly will I toil and suf-fer, On-ly let me walk with Thee.
D.S.-Then the gate of life e-ter-nal May I en-ter, Lord, with Thee.

CLOSE TO THEE
Refrain
D. S.
Close to Thee, close to Thee, Close to Thee, close to Thee;
49
RESCUE THE PERISHING
Fanny J. Crosby
COPYRIGHT PROPERTY OF W. H. DOANE. USED BY PERMISSION
William H. Doane
1. Res - cue the per-ish-ing, Care for the dy-ing, Snatch them in pit - y from
2. Tho' they are slighting Him, Still He is wait - ing, Wait-ing the pen - i - tent
3. Down in the human heart, Crushed by the tempter, Feelings lie bur - ied that
4. Res - cue the per-ish-ing, Du - ty demands it; Strength for thy la - bor the
sin and the grave; Weep o'er the err - ing one, Lift up the fall - en,
child to re - ceive; Plead with them earn-est-ly, Plead with them gen - tly;
grace can re - store; Touched by a lov-ing heart, Wak-ened by kind - ness,
Lord will pro - vide; Back to the narrow way Pa - tient - ly win them;
Chorus
Tell them of Je - sus the might-y to save.
He will for-give if they on - ly be-lieve.
Chords that are bro - ken will vi-brate once more.
Tell the poor wand'rer a Sav - ior has died.
Res - cue the per - ish-ing,
Care for the dy - ing; Je - sus is mer - ci - ful, Je - sus will save.

50 A MIGHTY FORTRESS IS OUR GOD

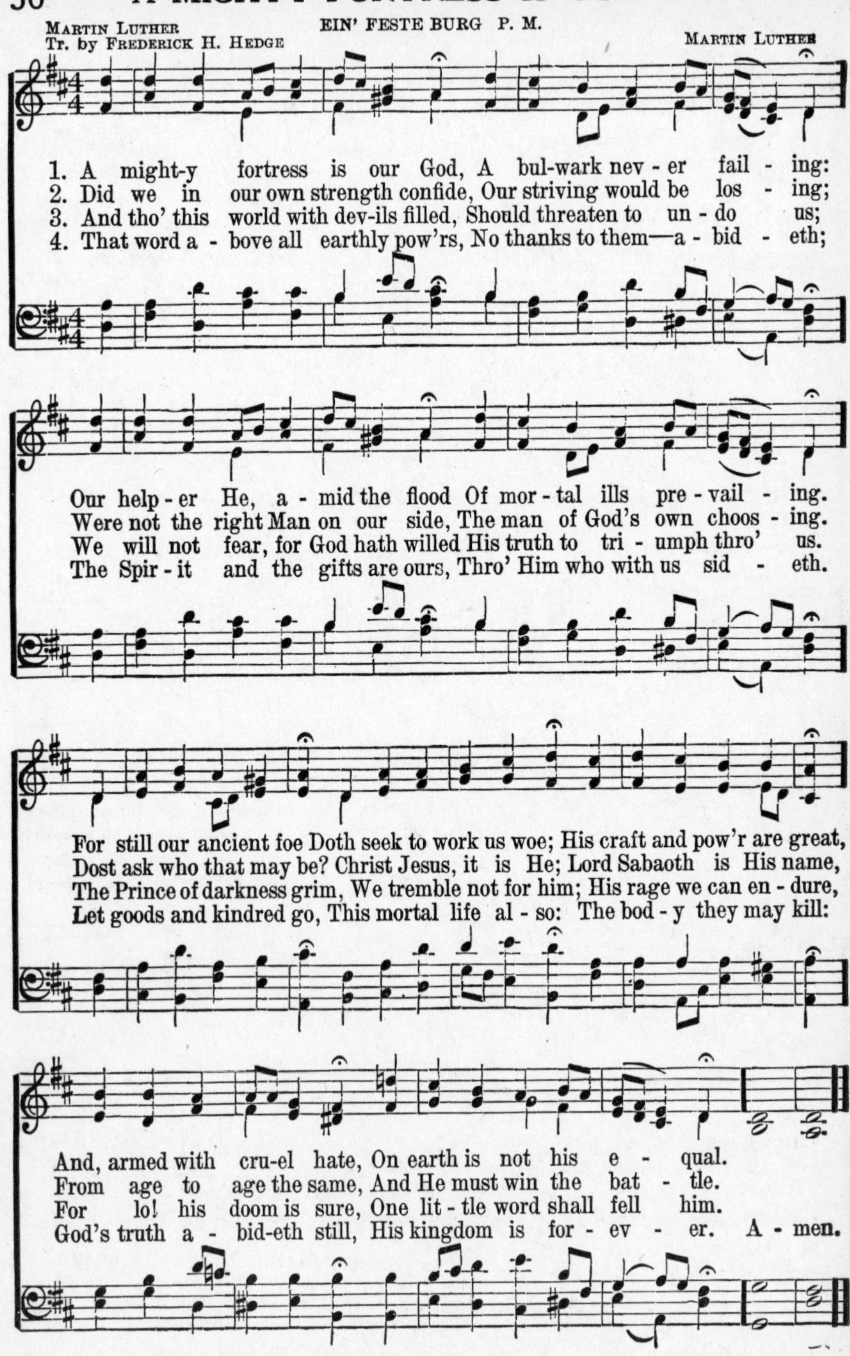

MARTIN LUTHER
Tr. by FREDERICK H. HEDGE
EIN' FESTE BURG P. M.
MARTIN LUTHER
1. A mighty-y fortress is our God, A bul-wark nev - er fail - ing:
2. Did we in our own strength confide, Our striving would be los - ing;
3. And tho' this world with dev-ils filled, Should threaten to un - do us;
4. That word a - bove all earthly pow'rs, No thanks to them—a - bid - eth;
Our help-er He, a - mid the flood Of mor-tal ills pre - vail - ing.
Were not the right Man on our side, The man of God's own choos - ing.
We will not fear, for God hath willed His truth to tri - umph thro' us.
The Spir - it and the gifts are ours, Thro' Him who with us sid - eth.
For still our ancient foe Doth seek to work us woe; His craft and pow'r are great,
Dost ask who that may be? Christ Jesus, it is He; Lord Sabaoth is His name,
The Prince of darkness grim, We tremble not for him; His rage we can en - dure,
Let goods and kindred go, This mortal life al - so: The bod - y they may kill:
And, armed with cru-el hate, On earth is not his e - qual.
From age to age the same, And He must win the bat - tle.
For lo! his doom is sure, One lit - tle word shall fell him.
God's truth a - bid-eth still, His kingdom is for - ev - er. A - men.

51 COME, YE THANKFUL PEOPLE

Henry Alford
George J. Elvey
1. Come, ye thank-ful peo-ple, come, Raise the song of har-vest-home:
2. All the world is God's own field, Fruit un-to His praise to yield;
3. For the Lord our God shall come, And shall take His har-vest home;
4. E-ven so, Lord, quick-ly come To Thy fi-nal har-vest-home;
All is safe-ly gath-ered in, Ere the win-ter storms be-gin;
Wheat and tares to-geth-er sown, Un-to joy or sor-row grown;
From His field shall in that day All of-fens-es purge a-way;
Gath-er Thou Thy peo-ple in, Free from sor-row, free from sin;
God, our Ma-ker, doth pro-vide For our wants to be sup-plied:
First the blade, and then the ear, Then the full corn shall ap-pear:
Give His an-gels charge at last In the fire the tares to cast;
There, for-ev-er pu-ri-fied, In Thy pres-ence to a-bide:
Come to God's own tem-ple, come, Raise the song of har-vest-home.
Lord of har-vest, grant that we Wholesome grain and pure may be.
But the fruit-ful ears to store In His gar-ner ev-er-more.
Come, with all Thine an-gels, come, Raise the glo-rious har-vest-home.

GOOD NIGHT AND GOOD MORNING

Lizzie DeArmond

Homer A. Rodeheaver

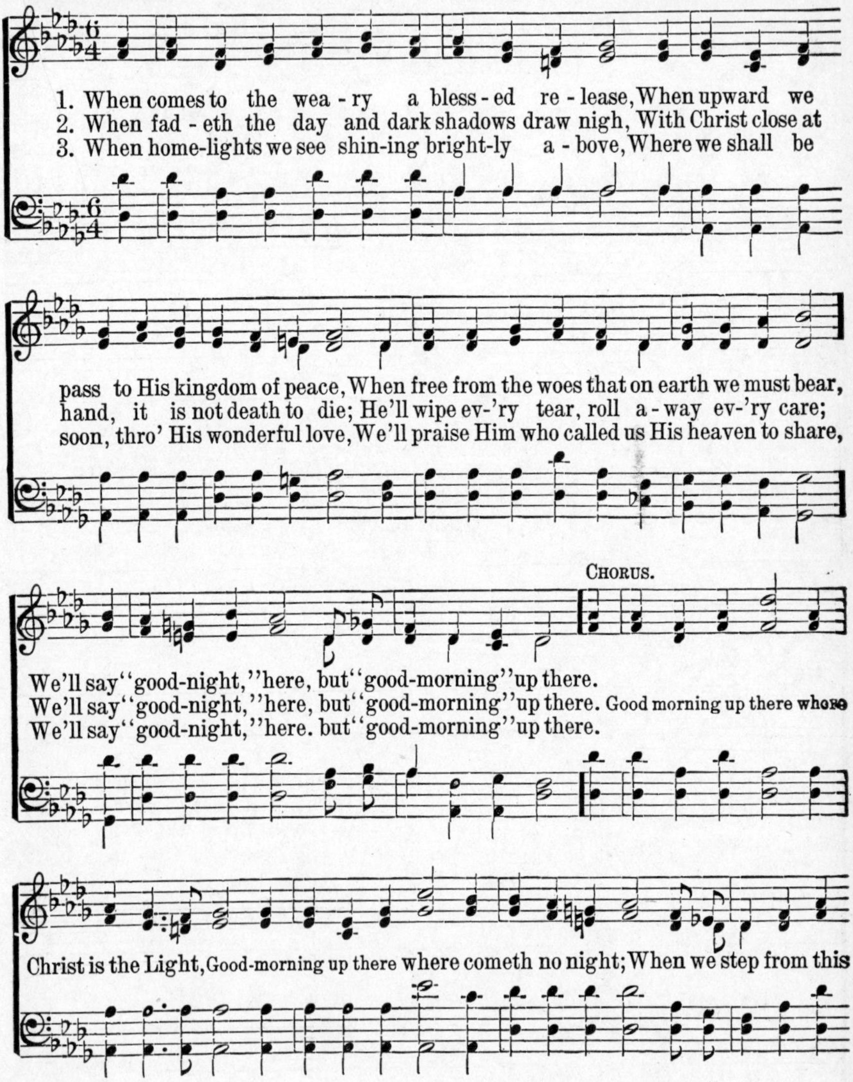

1. When comes to the wea - ry a bless - ed re - lease, When upward we pass to His kingdom of peace, When free from the woes that on earth we must bear, We'll say "good-night," here, but "good-morning" up there.
2. When fad - eth the day and dark shadows draw nigh, With Christ close at hand, it is not death to die; He'll wipe ev-'ry tear, roll a - way ev-'ry care; We'll say "good-night," here, but "good-morning" up there.
3. When home-lights we see shin-ing bright-ly a - bove, Where we shall be soon, thro' His wonderful love, We'll praise Him who called us His heaven to share, We'll say "good-night," here. but "good-morning" up there.

CHORUS.

Good morning up there where Christ is the Light, Good-morning up there where cometh no night; When we step from this earth to God's heaven so fair, We'll say "good-night" here, but "good-morning" up there.

53 THE CHURCH BY THE SIDE OF THE ROAD

Rev. W. C. Poole
B. D. Ackley
1. Thro' the mist of years I can seem to see The church of my childhood
2. And the old, old songs that we used to sing, I'm sing-ing them o'er and
3. At the place of pray'r, in that lit - tle church, I knelt at my mother's
4. There's a hal-lowed spot 'neath the old pine tree, Where mother was laid to
days; And it's mem-'ries sweet, so with joy re - plete, Shall live in my
o'er; They give strength and cheer, when the clouds draw near, And lead to the
side, There the Lord I found, it is ho - ly ground, The One who for
rest; What a joy 'twill be her dear face to see, With Him that I
heart al - way.
oth - er shore.
sin - ners died.
love the best.
CHORUS. (First four measures old melody.)
Then on mem - o - ry's page I can see a - gain, The
church by the side of the road; And wher-ev - er I
roam, it is guid-ing me home, The church by the side of the road.

54 I'LL GO WHERE YOU WANT ME TO GO

MARY BROWN

CARRIE E. ROUNSEFELL

1. It may not be on the mountain height, Or o - ver the storm - y sea,
2. Perhaps to - day there are lov - ing words Which Jesus would have me speak;
3. There's surely somewhere a low - ly place In earth's harvest fields so wide,
It may not be at the bat - tle's front My Lord will have need of me;
There may be now in the paths of sin Some wand'rer whom I should seek:
Where I may la - bor thro' life's short day For Je - sus, the Cru - ci - fied;
But if, by a still, small voice He calls To paths that I do not know,
O Sav - ior, if Thou wilt be my guide, Tho' dark and rug-ged the way,
So trust-ing my all to Thy ten-der care, And knowing Thou lov - est me,
I'll answer, dear Lord, with my hand in Thine, I'll go where you want me to go.
My voice shall ech - o the mes-sage sweet, I'll say what you want me to say.
I'll do Thy will with a heart sin-cere, I'll be what you want me to be.
REFRAIN
I'll go where you want me to go, dear Lord, Over mountain, or plain, or sea;

I'LL GO WHERE YOU WANT ME TO GO
I'll say what you want me to say, dear Lord, I'll be what you want me to be.
55
GOD BE WITH YOU
J. E. Rankin
W. G. Tomer
1. God be with you till we meet a-gain; By His counsels guide, uphold you,
2. God be with you till we meet a-gain; 'Neath His wings protecting hide you,
3. God be with you till we meet a-gain; When life's perils thick confound you,
4. God be with you till we meet a-gain; Keep love's banner floating o'er you,
With His sheep se-cure-ly fold you; God be with you till we meet a-gain.
Dai-ly man-na still pro-vide you; God be with you till we meet a-gain.
Put His arms un-fail-ing round you; God be with you till we meet a-gain.
Smite death's threat'ning wave before you; God be with you till we meet a-gain.
Chorus
Till we meet,......... till we meet, Till we meet at Je-sus' feet;
Till we meet, till we meet, till we meet;
Till we meet,......... till we meet, God be with you till we meet a-gain.
Till we meet, till we meet,

ONWARD, CHRISTIAN SOLDIERS

SABINE BARING-GOULD ARTHUR SULLIVAN

1. On-ward, Christian sol - diers! Marching as to war, With the cross of Je - sus Go-ing on be - fore; Christ, the roy - al Mas - ter, Leads a-gainst the foe; For-ward in - to bat - tle, See, His banners go!
2. Like a might-y ar - my Moves the Church of God; Brothers, we are tread - ing Where the saints have trod; We are not di - vid - ed, All one bod - y we; One in hope and doc - trine, One in char - i - ty.
3. Crowns and thorns may per-ish, Kingdoms rise and wane; But the Church of Je - sus Con-stant will re - main; Gates of hell can nev - er 'Gainst that Church prevail; We have Christ's own promise, Which can never fail.
4. On-ward, then, ye peo - ple! Join our happy throng; Blend with ours your voic - es In the tri-umph song; Glo - ry, laud, and hon - or, Un - to Christ the King; This thro' countless a - ges Men and an - gels sing.

CHORUS

On-ward, Chris-tian sol - diers! March-ing as to war, With the cross of Je - sus Go - ing on be - fore.

57 WE PLOUGH THE FIELDS, AND SCATTER

MATTHIAS CLAUDIUS **DRESDEN.** 7, 6, 7, 6. With Refrain

TR. JANE M. CAMPBELL JOHANN A. P. SCHULZ

1. We plough the fields, and scat-ter The good seed on the land, But it is
2. He on - ly is the Mak - er Of all things near and far; He paints the
3. We thank Thee, then, O Fa - ther, For all things bright and good; The seed-time

fed and wa - tered By God's al-might - y hand; He sends the snow in
way-side flow - er, He lights the ev-'ning star; The winds and waves o -
and the har - vest, Our life, our health, our food; No gifts have we to

win - ter, The warmth to swell the grain, The breez-es and the sun - shine.
bey Him, By Him the birds are fed; Much more to us, His chil - dren,
of - fer For all Thy love im-parts, But that which Thou de - sir - est,

And soft refreshing rain.
He gives our dai - ly bread.
Our hum-ble, thankful hearts.

REFRAIN

All good gifts around us Are sent from heav'n a-
bove; Then thank the Lord, O thank the Lord for all His love. A-men.

THERE ARE FOUR IN OUR FAMILY

Last week I hitched up the mare and drove up to Wheelbrook Center to call on the Saunders. Mr. Saunders had been ailing for a long time, and Mrs. Saunders was out doing the chores. Tagging along and doing the best he could to help her, was Billy. Billy's about nine, I guess.

I made it a point to spend the afternoon with them 'cause they've been pretty hard hit of late. Last month pneumonia caught a holt of Billy's twin brother, Jack, and they lost him.

We sort of puttered around, doing this and that; and while we was in the barn Mrs. Saunders set down on the grain bin and I set on the floor, and we had a little chat.

While we was talking, she told me a story about Billy that kind of stuck with me, and that's what I had in mind telling you about.

It seems that he was pretty proud of having a twin brother, Jack, and when he'd get to squabbling with the other young ones he'd say, "There's four in our family. Mother and Daddy and Jack and me." After Jack died Billy was so much in the habit of saying there was four in his family, he'd say it without thinking. The other young ones would say, "There's only three of you now," but Billy would keep saying, "There's four. Mother and Daddy—and—and me."

They'd laugh at him and tell him he couldn't count straight; but Billy stuck to it that there was four in his family. Even his mother had to tell him there were only three now. He couldn't seem to believe it, though.

One day he come legging it home from school for dear life and hollered to his mother half way across the barnyard, "Ma, aint' Jesus with us all the time?"

"Of course He is, Billy," she sez.

"There," he sez, beaming all over, "I told you there was four in our family."

Well, sir, when Mrs. Saunders got through telling me that story I guess there were tears in the eyes of both of us. There weren't much praying apparatus in the barn, but we got down on our knees out there by the hay and had a little talk with the fourth member of Billy's family.

When I got home that night I couldn't stop thinking about it; and when I set down to the old melodian a little tune came to me that went something like this.

58 THERE'S FOUR IN OUR FAMILY

SETH PARKER PHILLIPS H. LORD

1. For there's four in our fam - i - ly,...... Moth - er and Dad - dy and
2. For there's four in our fam - i - ly,...... Moth - er and Dad - dy and
me.......... Some think there's three, But I know there's more. There's
me.......... Some-times we three Will all say a pray'r, The
four in our fam - i - ly,......... 'Cause Je - sus is with us each
pray'r of our fam - i - ly......... It's nice for the folks who are
day,...... And Je - sus is with us each night; So Moth - er and
old,...... But my pray'r, when my hands I fold, Is, "Make me, Lord
Dad - dy And Je - sus and me Makes four in our fam - i - ly.........
Je - sus, Like you were, dear Lord, When you were but nine years old."....

59 BRIGHTLY GLEAMS OUR BANNER
Thomas J. Potter
ST. THERESA 6s 5s D With Refrain
Arthur S. Sullivan
1. Brightly gleams our banner, Pointing to the sky, Waving wand'rers onward
2. Je - sus, Lord and Master, At Thy sa-cred feet, Here with hearts rejoicing
3. All our days di-rect us In the way we go; Lead us on vic-to - rious
4. Then with saints and angels May we join a - bove, Off'ring pray'rs and praises
To their home on high. Journeying o'er the des-ert, Glad-ly thus we pray,
See Thy children meet; Oft - en have we left Thee, Oft - en gone a - stray;
O - ver ev - 'ry foe; Bid Thine angels shield us When the storm clouds low'r;
At Thy throne of love; When the toil is o - ver, Then come rest and peace;
Refrain
And with hearts u-nit-ed Take our heav'nward way.
Keep us, mighty Sav-ior, In the nar - row way. Brightly gleams our banner
Par-don, Lord, and save us In the last dread hour.
Je - sus in His beauty, Songs that never cease,
Pointing to the sky, Waving wand'rers onward To their home on high. Amen.

60 FROM GREENLAND'S ICY MOUNTAINS

REGINALD HEBER | LOWELL MASON

1. From Greenland's i - cy mountains, From In - dia's cor - al strand;
2. What though the spi - cy breez - es Blow soft o'er Cey - lon's isle;
3. Shall we, whose souls are light - ed With wis - dom from on high,
4. Waft, waft, ye winds, His sto - ry, And you, ye wa - ters, roll,
Where Af - ric's sun - ny fount - ains Roll down their gold - en sand:
Though ev - 'ry pros-pect pleas - es, And on - ly man is vile?
Shall we to men be - night - ed The lamp of life de - ny?
Till, like a sea of glo - ry, It spreads from pole to pole:
From man - y an an - cient riv - er, From man - y a palm-y plain,
In vain with lav - ish kind - ness The gifts of God are strown;
Sal - va - tion! O sal - va - tion! The joy - ful sound pro - claim,
Till o'er our ran-somed na - ture The Lamb for sin - ners slain,
They call us to de - liv - er Their land from er - ror's chain.
The heathen in his blind - ness Bows down to wood and stone.
Till earth's re - mot - est na - tion Has learned Mes - si - ah's name.
Re - deem-er, King, Cre - a - tor, In bliss re - turns to reign. A-men.

61 THE LILY OF THE VALLEY

English Melody

1. I have found a friend in Je - sus, He's ev - 'ry-thing to me, He's the
2. He all my griefs has tak - en, and all my sor - rows borne; In temp -
3. He will nev - er, nev - er leave me, nor yet for-sake me here, While I

fair - est of ten thou-sand to my soul; The Lil - y of the Val - ley,
ta - tion He's my strong and might-y tow'r; I have all for Him for-sak - en,
live by faith and do His bless-ed will; A wall of fire a - bout me,

D.S.—Lil - y of the Val - ley,

Fine.

in Him a - lone I see All I need to cleanse and make me ful - ly whole.
and all my i - dols torn From my heart, and now He keeps me by His pow'r.
I've noth-ing now to fear, With His man - na He my hun - gry soul shall fill.

the Bright and Morn-ing Star, He's the fair - est of ten thou-sand to my soul.

In sor - row He's my com - fort, in trou - ble He's my stay,
Though all the world for - sake me, and Sa - tan tempt me sore,
Then sweep - ing up to glo - ry to see His bless - ed face,

D.S.
He tells me ev - 'ry care on Him to roll. He's tbe
Through Je - sus I shall safe - ly reach the goal. He's the
Where riv - ers of de - light shall ev - er roll. He's the

62 THE CHURCH IN THE WILDWOOD

W. S. P. Dr. WM. S. PITTS

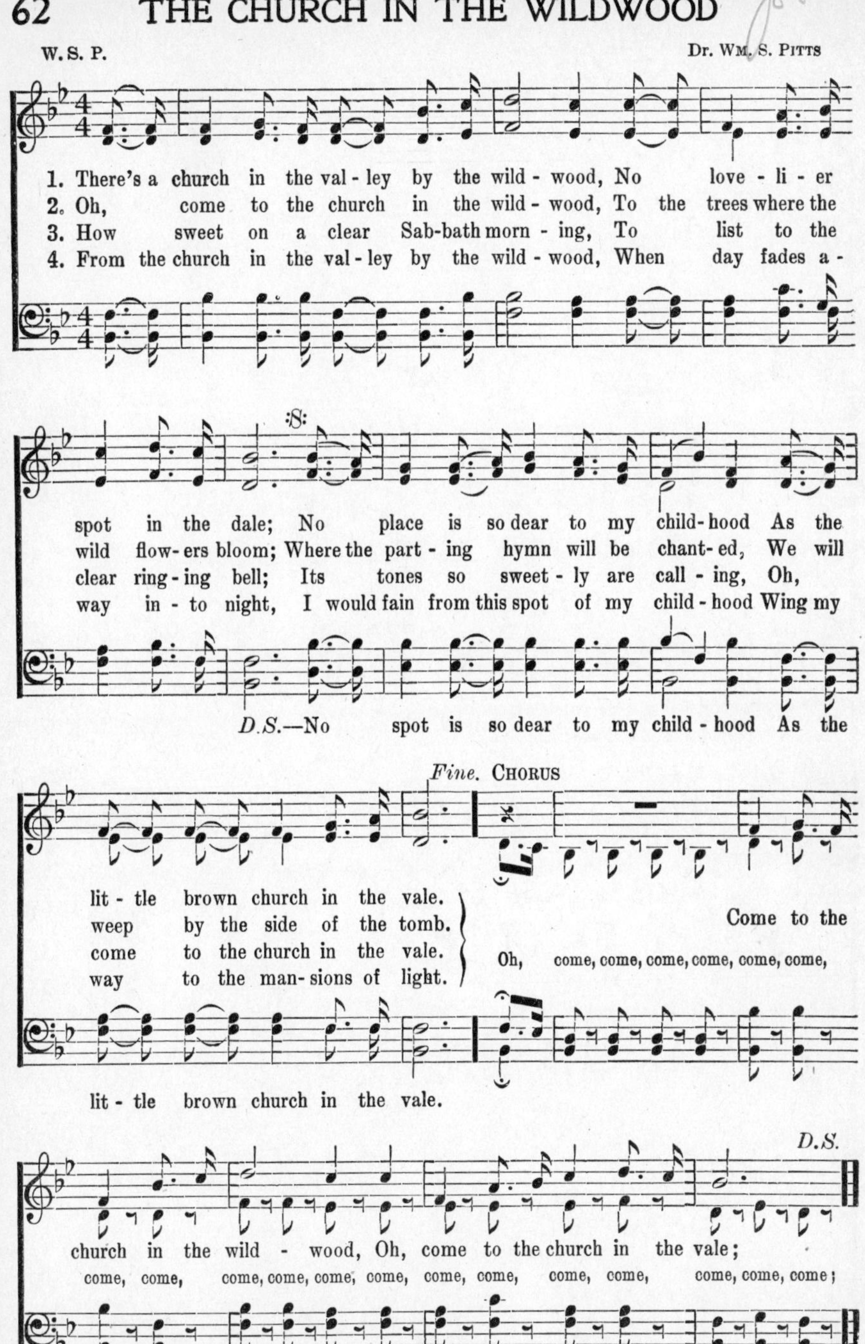
1. There's a church in the val - ley by the wild - wood, No love - li - er
2. Oh, come to the church in the wild - wood, To the trees where the
3. How sweet on a clear Sab-bath morn - ing, To list to the
4. From the church in the val - ley by the wild - wood, When day fades a -
spot in the dale; No place is so dear to my child- hood As the
wild flow- ers bloom; Where the part - ing hymn will be chant- ed, We will
clear ring - ing bell; Its tones so sweet - ly are call - ing, Oh,
way in - to night, I would fain from this spot of my child - hood Wing my
D.S.—No spot is so dear to my child - hood As the
Fine. CHORUS
lit - tle brown church in the vale.
weep by the side of the tomb.
come to the church in the vale.
way to the man- sions of light.
Come to the
Oh, come, come, come, come, come, come,
lit - tle brown church in the vale.
D.S.
church in the wild - wood, Oh, come to the church in the vale;
come, come, come, come, come, come, come, come, come, come, come, come, come;

63

THE BIRD WITH A BROKEN WING

Dedicated to Thomas Elgar

HEZEKIAH BUTTERWORTH
F. M. LAMB

1. I walked thro' the woodland mead-ows, Where sweet the thrushes sing;
2. I found a young life bro - ken By sin's se-duc-tive art;
3. But the bird with a bro - ken pin - ion Kept an-oth - er from the snare;
And found on a bed of moss - es, A bird with a bro- ken wing.
And touch'd with a Christ-like pit - y I took him to my heart.
And the life that sin had strick - en Rais'd an - oth - er from de - spair.
I healed its wound, and each morn-ing It sang its old sweet strain;
He lived with a no - ble pur - pose, And strug-gled not in vain;
For Christ, the might - y Heal - er, Has a balm for ev - 'ry pain;
But the bird with a bro - ken pin - ion Nev - er soared so high a - gain.
But the life that sin had strick- en, Nev - er soared so high a - gain.
And the soul that He has heal - ed, High - er still may rise a - gain.

64 TRUST AND OBEY

J. H. SAMMIS — D. B. TOWNER

1. When we walk with the Lord In the light of His Word What a glo - ry He
2. Not a shad-ow can rise, Not a cloud in the skies, But His smile quickly
3. Not a bur-den we bear, Not a sor - row we share, But our toil He doth
4. But we nev - er can prove The de-lights of His love Un - til all on the
5. Then in fel - low-ship sweet We will sit at His feet, Or we'll walk by His
sheds on our way! While we do His good will, He a-bides with us still,
drives it a - way; Not a doubt nor a fear, Not a sigh nor a tear,
rich - ly re - pay; Not a grief nor a loss, Not a frown nor a cross,
al - tar we lay; For the fa - vor He shows, And the joy He be-stows,
side in the way; What He says we will do, Where He sends we will go,—
CHORUS
And with all who will trust and o - bey.
Can a - bide while we trust and o - bey.
But is blest if we trust and o - bey.
Are for them who will trust and o - bey.
Nev - er fear, on - ly trust and o - bey.
Trust and o- bey, for there's no oth- er
way To be hap - py in Je - sus, but to trust and o - bey.

65 HAS ANYBODY FOUND A TROUBLE?

Copyright, 1930, by PHILLIPS H. LORD
SETH PARKER
PHILLIPS H. LORD
1. I had a mess of trou - bles That were trou-bling me, And each one was a thor - ough - bred, With a great long ped - i - gree; But now I've gone and lost one, I've had since in - fan - cy; I thought my chron - ic trou - ble
2. Don't think that I am lone - some, 'Cause no one calls on me; I have a mess of trou - bles, That are my com - pa - ny; But now I find I've lost one, I've had since in - fan - cy; My dear old chron - ic trou - ble

HAS ANYBODY FOUND A TROUBLE?

CHORUS
Would have more loy - al - ty.
Has sim - ply ceased to be.
Has an - y - bod - y found a
trou - ble, The trou- ble that be-longs to me? It was as big a
trou - ble, As trou - bles ev - er grow to be; You
say you've found a small one? One you can hard - ly see? Why,
that must be the trou - ble, The trou- ble that be-longs to me.

66 IF YOUR HEART KEEPS RIGHT

Lizzie DeArmond — B. D. Ackley

1. If the dark shadows gath-er As you go a - long, Do not grieve for their com - ing, Sing a cheer - y song, There is joy for the tak - ing it will soon be light—Ev - 'ry cloud wears a rainbow If your heart keeps right.
2. Is your life just a tan-gle Full of toil and care? Smile a bit as you jour - ney, Others' bur-dens share; You'll for - get all your troubles, Making their lives bright, Skies will grow blue and sun-ny If your heart keeps right.
3. There are blossoms of gladness 'Neath the winter's snow, From the gloom and the darkness Comes the morning's glow; Nev-er give up the bat - tle, You will win the fight, Gain the rest of the Vic-tor, If your heart keeps right.
CHORUS
If your heart keeps right, If your heart keeps right, There's a song of glad-ness in the dark - est night; If your heart keeps right, If your

IF YOUR HEART KEEPS RIGHT
heart keeps right, Ev - 'ry cloud will wear a rain-bow, If your heart keeps right.
67
BLESSED ASSURANCE
FANNY J. CROSBY
Used by permission
MRS. JOS. F. KNAPP
1. Blessed as-sur-ance, Je-sus is mine! O what a foretaste of glo-ry di - vine!
2. Per-fect submission, perfect de - light, Visions of rapture now burst on my sight!
3. Per-fect submission, all is at rest, I in my Sav-ior am happy and blest;
Heir of sal-va-tion, purchase of God, Born of His Spir-it, wash'd in His blood.
An - gels de-scending, bring from a - bove Echoes of mer-cy, whispers of love.
Watching and waiting, looking a - bove, Fill'd with His goodness, lost in His love.
CHORUS
This is my sto - ry, this is my song, Praising my Sav-ior all the day long;
This is my sto - ry, this is my song, Praising my Sav-ior all the day long.

68 TRUE HEARTED, WHOLE HEARTED

Copyright, 1916, by Geo. C. Stebbins Renewal
Hope Publishing Co., owners
FRANCES R. HAVERGAL
GEORGE C. STEBBINS
1. True-hearted, whole-hearted, faithful and loy - al, King of our lives by Thy
2. True-hearted, whole-hearted, full-est al-le-giance, Yielding henceforth to our
3. True-hearted, whole-hearted, Sav-ior all-glo-rious! Take Thy great power and
grace we will be; Un - der the stan-dard ex - alt - ed and roy - al, Strong
glo - ri -ous King; Val - iant en-deav - or and lov - ing o - be-dience Free-
reign there a - lone, O - ver our wills and af - fec - tions vic-tor-ious, Free-
in Thy strength we will bat-tle for Thee.
ly and joy - ous - ly now we would bring.
ly sur-ren-dered and whol-ly Thine own.
CHORUS
Peal out the watchword! silence it
Peal
si-lence
nev - er, Song of our spir-its re - joic - ing and free; Peal out the
Song
re-joic-ing and
free;
Peal
watchword! loy - al for-ev - er, King of our lives, by Thy grace we will be.
loy - al
King

69 DO SOMETHING FOR OTHERS

C. H. G. CHAS. H. GABRIEL

1. Man-y a soul in the bat-tle of life Trembles with fear at the din and the strife, Bear-ing a-lone, a-mid tri-al and care, Bur-dens and sor-rows God bids you to share.
2. Man-y in doubt or in fear of the way Mute-ly ap-peal for your guid-ance to-day; On your de-mean-or the choice may de-pend— Are you concerned for the stran-ger or friend?
3. Man-y, dis-heartened by cru-el de-ceit, Bro-ken and worn by the pangs of de-feat, Doubt-ing, de-spair-ing-ly, help-less-ly stand, Wait-ing, per-haps, for your strengthen-ing hand.
4. Man-y are turn-ing a-way from the right In-to the maze of the shad-ows of night; Go to them, speak to them, o-ver them pray, Help them, support them—do something to-day.
rit.
CHORUS
Do something for oth-ers,...... Something for oth-ers to-day!......... Du-ty de-mands it, And Je-sus commands it! Do something for oth-ers to-day.
Something for oth-ers, do something for oth-ers, Do something for oth-ers to-day!

70 ABIDE WITH ME

H. F. Lyte
W. H. Monk
1. A - bide with me: fast falls the e - ven - tide; The dark - ness deep - ens; Lord, with me a - bide: When oth - er help - ers fail, and com - forts flee, Help of the help - less, O a - bide with me!
2. Swift to its close ebbs out life's lit - tle day; Earth's joys grow dim, its glo - ries pass a - way; Change and de - cay in all a - round I see: O Thou who chang - est not, a - bide with me!
3. I need Thy pres - ence ev - 'ry pass - ing hour: What but Thy grace can foil the tempt - er's pow'r? Who like Thy - self my guide and stay can be? Through cloud and sun - shine, O a - bide with me!
4. Hold Thou Thy cross be - fore my clos - ing eyes, Shine thro' the gloom, and point me to the skies: Heav'n's morning breaks, and earth's vain shad - ows flee— In life, in death, O Lord, a - bide with me!
71
WHERE HE LEADS ME
COPYRIGHT, 1890, BY J. S. NORRIS
USED BY PERMISSION
E. W. Blandly
J. S. Norris
1. I can hear my Sav - ior call - ing, I can hear my Sav - ior call - ing,
2. I'll go with Him thro' the gar - den, I'll go with Him thro' the gar - den,
3. I'll go with Him thro' the judg - ment, I'll go with Him thro' the judg - ment,
4. He will give me grace and glo - ry, He will give me grace and glo - ry,

REF.—*Where He leads me I will fol - low, Where He leads me I will fol - low,*

WHERE HE LEADS ME

I can hear my Sav - ior call - ing, "Take thy cross and fol-low, fol - low Me."
I'll go with Him thro' the gar - den, I'll go with Him, with Him all the way.
I'll go with Him thr.' the judg-ment, I'll go with Him, with Him all the way.
He will give me grace and glo - ry, And go with me, with me all the way.
Where He leads me I will fol - low, I'll go with Him, with Him all the way.
1. Sav - ior, Thy dy - ing love Thou gav - est me, Nor should I aught with-hold, Dear Lord, from Thee: In love my soul would bow, My heart ful - fill its vow, Some of-f'ring bring Thee now, Something for Thee.
2. At the blest mer - cy - seat, Plead-ing for me, My fee - ble faith looks up, Je - sus, to Thee: Help me the cross to bear, Thy wondrous love de-clare, Some song to raise, or prayer, Something for Thee.
3. Give me a faith - ful heart,—Like - ness to Thee,— That each de- part - ing day Hence-forth may see Some work of love be - gun, Some deed of kind-ness done, Some wand'rer sought and won, Something for Thee.
4. All that I am and have,—Thy gifts so free,— In joy, in grief, thro' life, Dear Lord, for Thee! And when Thy face I see, My ransomed soul shall be, Thro' all e - ter - ni - ty, Something for Thee.

72 SOMETHING FOR JESUS

S. D. PHELPS — ROBERT LOWRY

73 'TIS MIDNIGHT; AND ON OLIVE'S BROW
OLIVE'S BROW. L. M.
William B. Tappan
William B. Bradbury
1. 'Tis midnight; and on Ol - ive's brow The star is dimmed that late-ly shone:
2. 'Tis midnight; and from all re-moved The Sav - ior wrestles 'lone with fears;
3. 'Tis midnight; and for oth - ers' guilt The Man of Sor-rows weeps in blood;
4. 'Tis midnight; and from e-ther-plains Is borne the song that an - gels know;
'Tis midnight; in the gar - den now The suff'ring Sav-ior prays a - lone.
E'en that dis-ci - ple whom He loved Heeds not his Master's grief and tears.
Yet He that hath in an - guish knelt Is not for-sak - en by His God.
Un-heard by mor-tals are the strains That sweetly soothe the Sav-ior's woe.
74 REVIVE US AGAIN
Wm. P. Mackay
John J. Husband
1. We praise Thee, O God! for the Son of Thy love, For Je - sus who
2. We praise Thee, O God! for Thy Spir - it of light, Who has shown us our
3. All glo - ry and praise to the Lamb that was slain, Who has borne all our
4. Re - vive us a - gain; fill each heart with Thy love; May each soul be re-
died, and is now gone a - bove.
Sav - ior, and scat-tered our night.
sins, and has cleansed ev-'ry stain.
kin - dled with fire from a - bove.
CHORUS
Hal-le - lu - jah! Thine the glo-ry, Hal-le-

REVIVE US AGAIN
lu-jah! a-men; Hal-le-lu-jah! Thine the glo-ry, re-vive us a-gain.
75 WHAT A FRIEND
JOSEPH SCRIVEN
CHARLES C. CONVERSE
1. What a Friend we have in Je-sus, All our sins and griefs to bear!
2. Have we tri-als and temp-ta-tions? Is there trou-ble an-y-where?
3. Are we weak and heav-y-la-den, Cumbered with a load of care?—
What a priv-i-lege to car-ry Ev-'ry-thing to God in pray'r!
We should nev-er be dis-cour-aged, Take it to the Lord in pray'r.
Pre-cious Sav-ior, still our ref-uge,—Take it to the Lord in pray'r.
O what peace we oft-en for-feit, O what needless pain we bear,
Can we find a friend so faith-ful Who will all our sor-rows share?
Do thy friends despise, for-sake thee? Take it to the Lord in pray'r;
All because we do not car-ry Ev-'ry-thing to God in pray'r!
Je-sus knows our ev-'ry weak-ness, Take it to the Lord in pray'r.
In His arms He'll take and shield thee, Thou wilt find a sol-ace there.

76 ALL THE WAY TO CALVARY

A. H. A. Rev. A. H. Ackley

1. I do not ask for di - a - dem or scep - ter, I do not seek for
2. I know the path He trod is nev - er eas - y, It cost the Son of
3. I can-not turn a - side, for love im - pels me To drink the cup of
4. So trust-ing in His love, I'll toil and suf - fer, Sup-port - ed by His
world-ly joy or fame, I on - ly ask to fol - low my Re-deem - er, And
God His precious blood, It leads on to the cross of name-less an - guish, But
sor - row and of woe; But min-gled with the tears I find the com - fort, The
ev - er - last - ing grace, Un - til at last I rise complete, per - fect - ed, Trans-
tell a - broad the won-ders of His name.
ev - er climb-eth up-ward un - to God.
peace that on - ly Je - sus can be - stow.
formed to look up - on His bless - ed face.
CHORUS
I will trav - el all the way to
Cal - va - ry, I will walk the road that Jesus walk'd for me, I will serve Him to the
end, For He is my dearest friend, I will trav - el all the way to Cal - va - ry.

77 SOFTLY AND TENDERLY

W. L. T.
HOPE PUB. CO., OWNERS
WILL L. THOMPSON
Very slow pp
m
1. Soft - ly and ten-der - ly Je - sus is call-ing, Call - ing for you and for me;
2. Why should we tarry when Jesus is plead-ing, Pleading for you and for me?
3. Time is now fleeting, the moments are passing, Passing from you and from me;
4. Oh! for the won-der-ful love He has promised, Promised for you and for me;
See, on the portals He's waiting and watching, Watching for you and for me.
Why should we linger and heed not His mercies, Mer-cies for you and for me?
Shadows are gathering, death-beds are coming, Com-ing for you and for me.
Tho' we have sinned, He has mercy and pardon, Par-don for you and for me.
CHORUS m
cresc.
Come home,.. come home,..... Ye who are wear-y, come home;...
Come home, come home,
pp
ppp
rit.
pp
Ear-nest-ly, ten-der-ly, Je - sus is call-ing, Call-ing, O sin-ner, come home!

BENEATH THE CROSS OF JESUS

Elizabeth C. Clephane

Frederick C. Maker

1. Be-neath the cross of Je - sus I fain would take my stand,
2. Up - on that cross of Je - sus Mine eye at times can see
3. I take, O cross, thy shad - ow For my a - bid - ing place;
The shad - ow of a might - y rock With - in a wea - ry land;
The ver - y dy - ing form of One Who suf - fered there for me;
I ask no oth - er sun-shine than The sun - shine of His face;
A home with - in the wil - der - ness, A rest up - on the way,
And from my smit - ten heart with tears Two won - ders I con - fess,—
Con - tent to let the world go by, To know no gain or loss,
From the burning of the noon-tide heat, And the bur-den of the day.
The won - ders of His glo-rious love And my un-wor - thi - ness.
My sin - ful self my on - ly shame, My glo - ry all the cross.

79 GOD WILL TAKE CARE OF YOU

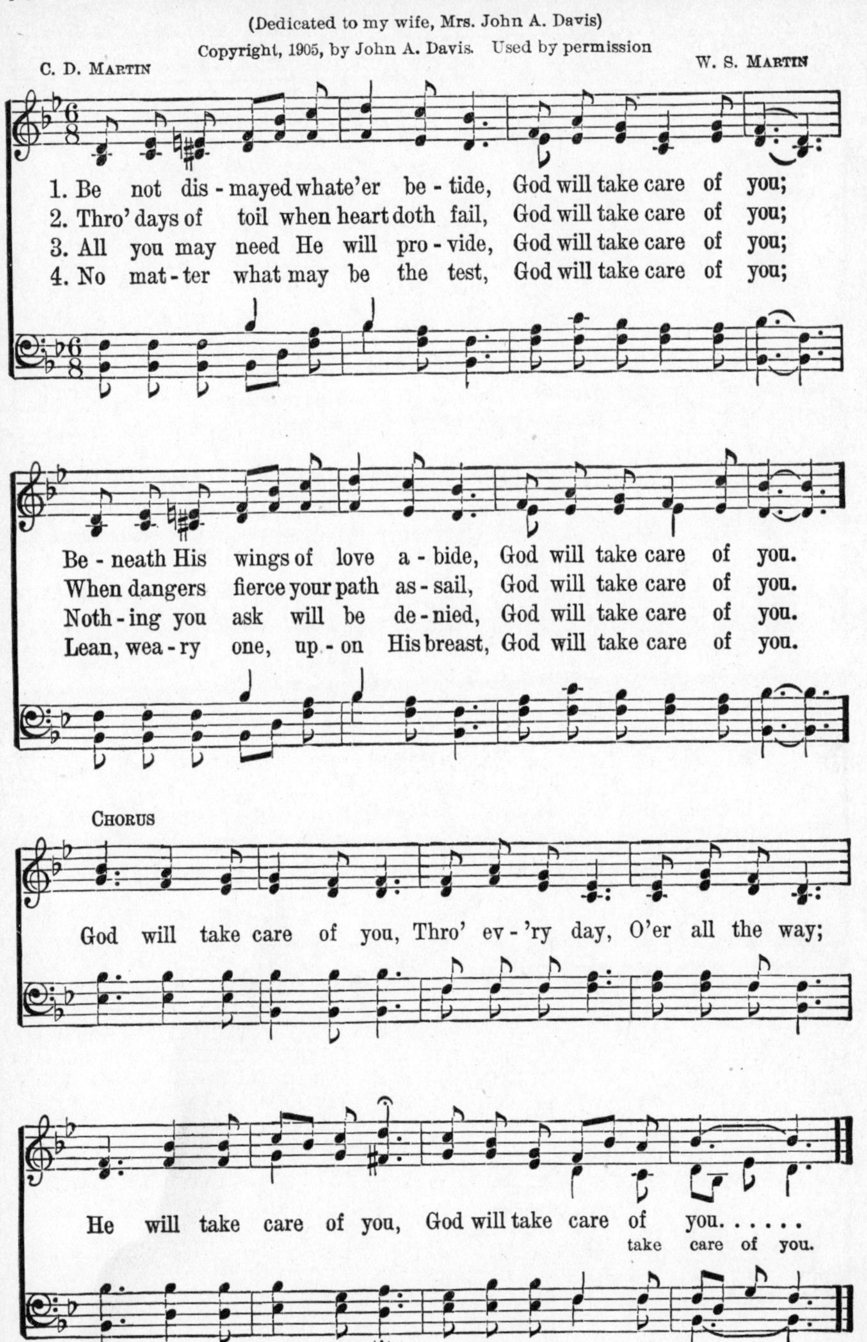
(Dedicated to my wife, Mrs. John A. Davis)
Copyright, 1905, by John A. Davis. Used by permission
C. D. Martin
W. S. Martin
1. Be not dis - mayed whate'er be - tide, God will take care of you;
2. Thro' days of toil when heart doth fail, God will take care of you;
3. All you may need He will pro - vide, God will take care of you;
4. No mat - ter what may be the test, God will take care of you;
Be - neath His wings of love a - bide, God will take care of you.
When dangers fierce your path as - sail, God will take care of you.
Noth - ing you ask will be de - nied, God will take care of you.
Lean, wea - ry one, up - on His breast, God will take care of you.
Chorus
God will take care of you, Thro' ev - 'ry day, O'er all the way;
He will take care of you, God will take care of you. . . . . .
take care of you.

I AM PRAYING FOR YOU

S. O'Maley Cluff — Ira D. Sankey

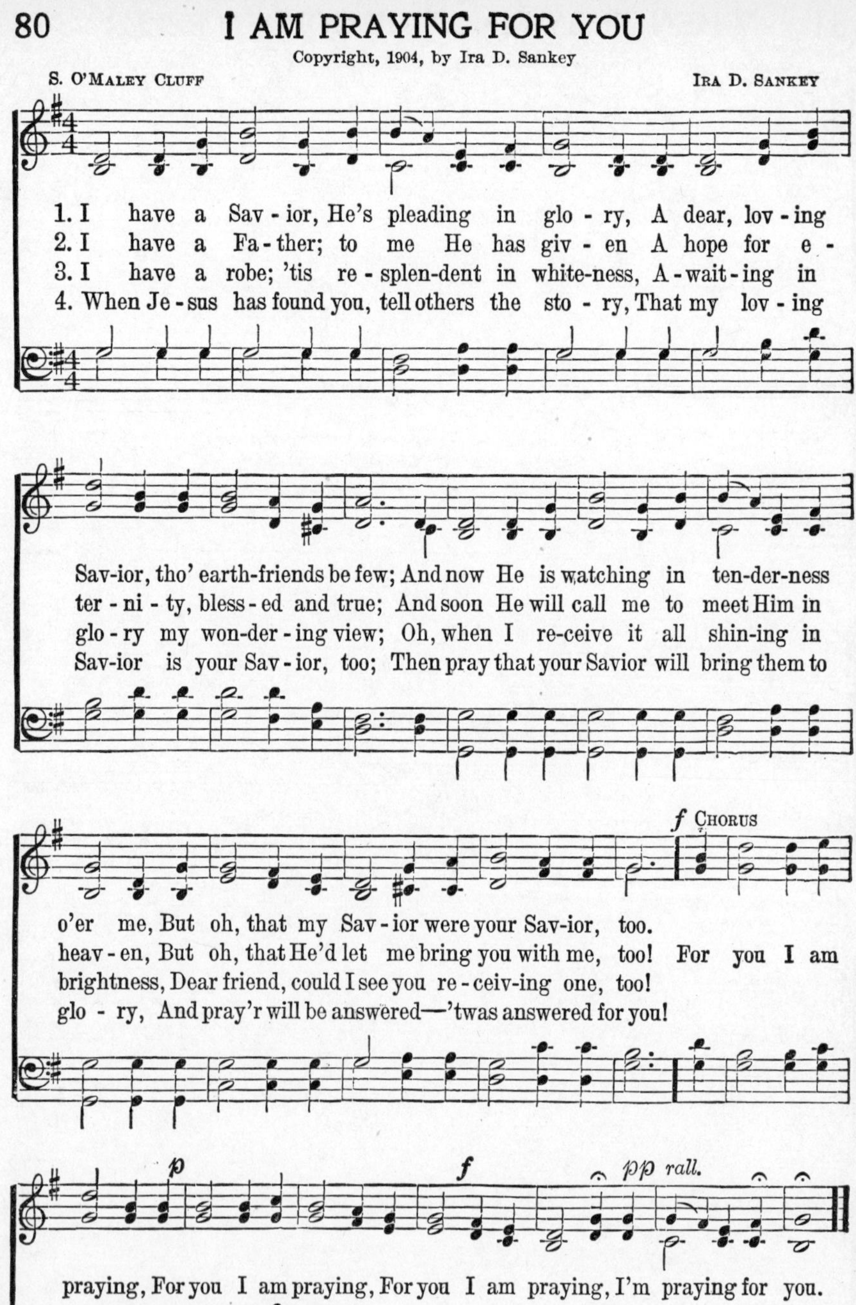
1. I have a Sav - ior, He's pleading in glo - ry, A dear, lov - ing Sav-ior, tho' earth-friends be few; And now He is watching in ten-der-ness o'er me, But oh, that my Sav - ior were your Sav-ior, too.
2. I have a Fa - ther; to me He has giv - en A hope for e - ter - ni - ty, bless - ed and true; And soon He will call me to meet Him in heav - en, But oh, that He'd let me bring you with me, too!
3. I have a robe; 'tis re - splen-dent in white-ness, A - wait - ing in glo - ry my won-der - ing view; Oh, when I re-ceive it all shin-ing in brightness, Dear friend, could I see you re - ceiv-ing one, too!
4. When Je - sus has found you, tell others the sto - ry, That my lov - ing Sav-ior is your Sav - ior, too; Then pray that your Savior will bring them to glo - ry, And pray'r will be answered—'twas answered for you!
f CHORUS
For you I am praying, For you I am praying, For you I am praying, I'm praying for you.
p
f
pp rall.

81 WHEN THEY RING THE GOLDEN BELLS

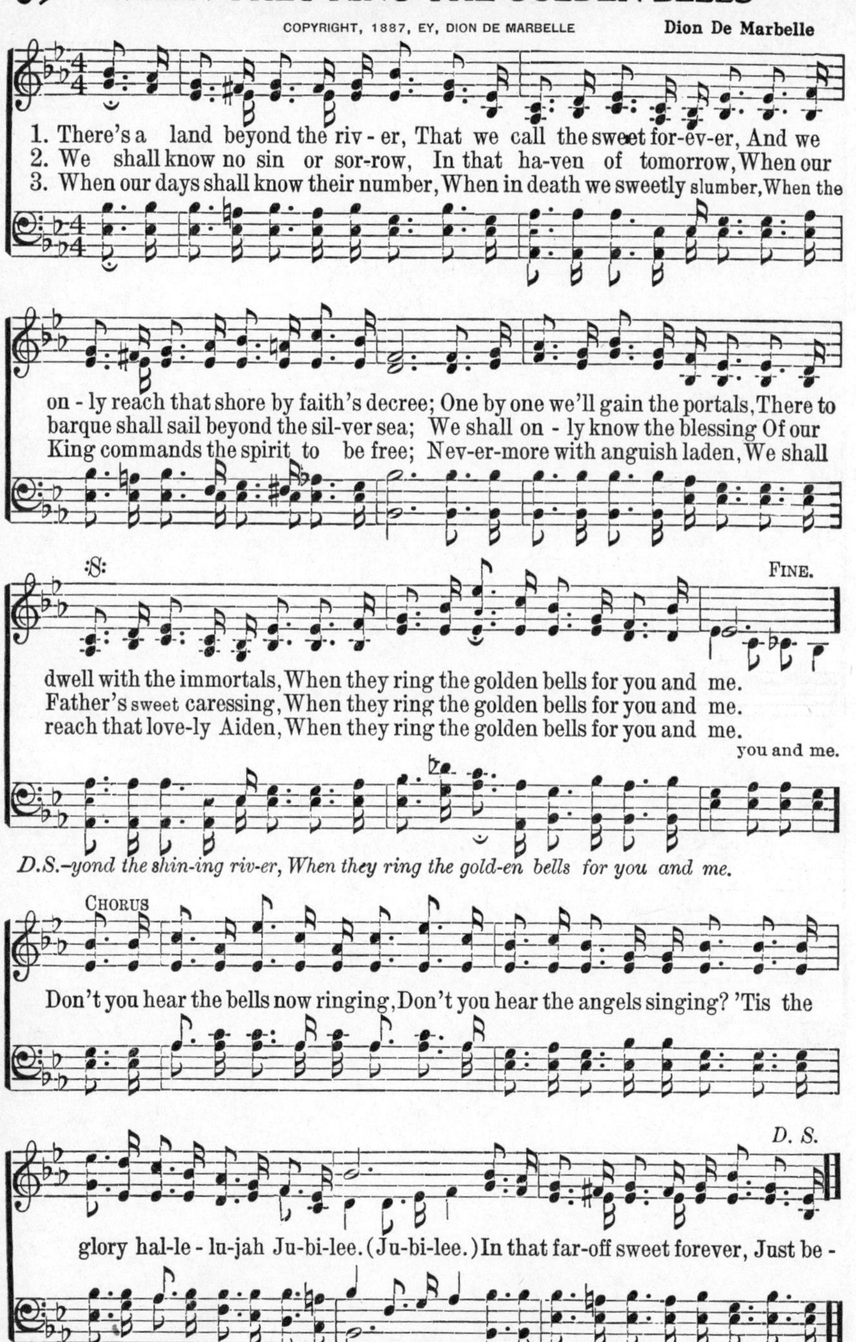

COPYRIGHT, 1887, BY, DION DE MARBELLE
Dion De Marbelle
1. There's a land beyond the riv - er, That we call the sweet for-ev-er, And we on - ly reach that shore by faith's decree; One by one we'll gain the portals, There to dwell with the immortals, When they ring the golden bells for you and me.
2. We shall know no sin or sor-row, In that ha-ven of tomorrow, When our barque shall sail beyond the sil-ver sea; We shall on - ly know the blessing Of our Father's sweet caressing, When they ring the golden bells for you and me.
3. When our days shall know their number, When in death we sweetly slumber, When the King commands the spirit to be free; Nev-er-more with anguish laden, We shall reach that love-ly Aiden, When they ring the golden bells for you and me.
you and me.
FINE.
D.S.–yond the shin-ing riv-er, When they ring the gold-en bells for you and me.
CHORUS
Don't you hear the bells now ringing, Don't you hear the angels singing? 'Tis the glory hal-le - lu-jah Ju-bi-lee. (Ju-bi-lee.) In that far-off sweet forever, Just be -
D. S.

82 O THOU IN WHOSE PRESENCE

Joseph Swain — Freeman Lewis

83 JESUS, SAVIOR, PILOT ME

Edward Hopper — J. E. Gould

1. O Thou in whose pres - ence my soul takes de - light, On whom in af - flic - tion I call, My com - fort by day, and my song in the night, My hope, my sal - va - tion, my all!
2. Where dost Thou, dear Shep - herd, re - sort with Thy sheep, To feed them in pas-tures of love? Say, why in the val - ley of death should I weep, Or a - lone in this wil - der - ness rove?
3. O why should I wan - der an a - lien from Thee, Or cry in the des - ert for bread? Thy foes will re - joice when my sor - rows they see, And smile at the tears I have shed.
4. Ye daughters of Zi - on, de - clare, have you seen The star that on Is - ra - el shone? Say, if in your tents my Be - lov - ed has been, And where with His flocks He is gone.
FINE.
1. Je - sus, Sav - ior, pi - lot me O - ver life's tem-pes-tuos sea;
D.C.—Chart and com - pass come from Thee, Je - sus, Sav - ior, pi - lot me.
2. As a moth - er stills her child, Thou canst hush the o-cean wild.
D.C.—Wondrous Sov-'reign of the sea; Je - sus, Sav - ior, pi - lot me.
3. When at last I near the shore, And the fear - ful breakers roar,
D.C.—May I hear Thee say to me; "Fear not, I will pi - lot thee."

JESUS, SAVIOR, PILOT ME

D. C.
Un-known waves a-round me roll, Hid - ing rocks and treach'rous shoal;
Boist'rous waves o - bey Thy will When Thou say'st to them be still!"
'Twixt me and the peaceful rest, Then, while lean - ing on Thy breast,
84 O DAY OF REST AND GLADNESS
Christopher Wordsworth
Arr. by Lowell Mason
1. O day of rest and gladness, O day of joy and light, O balm of care and sadness, Most beau-ti-ful, most bright: On Thee, the high and lowly, Thro' a - ges joined in tune, Sing "Holy, ho - ly, ho - ly," To the great God Tri-une.
2. On Thee, at the cre - a - tion, The light first had its birth; On Thee, for our salvation, Christ rose from depths of earth: On Thee, our Lord victorious, The Spirit sent from heav'n; And thus on Thee, most glorious, A triple light was given.
3. To-day on wea-ry na-tions The heav'nly manna falls; To ho - ly con-vo - ca - tion The sil - ver trumpet calls, Where gospel light is glowing With pure and radiant beams, And living water flow-ing With soul re-fresh-ing streams.

85 SINCE JESUS CAME INTO MY HEART

R. H. McDaniel — Chas. H. Gabriel

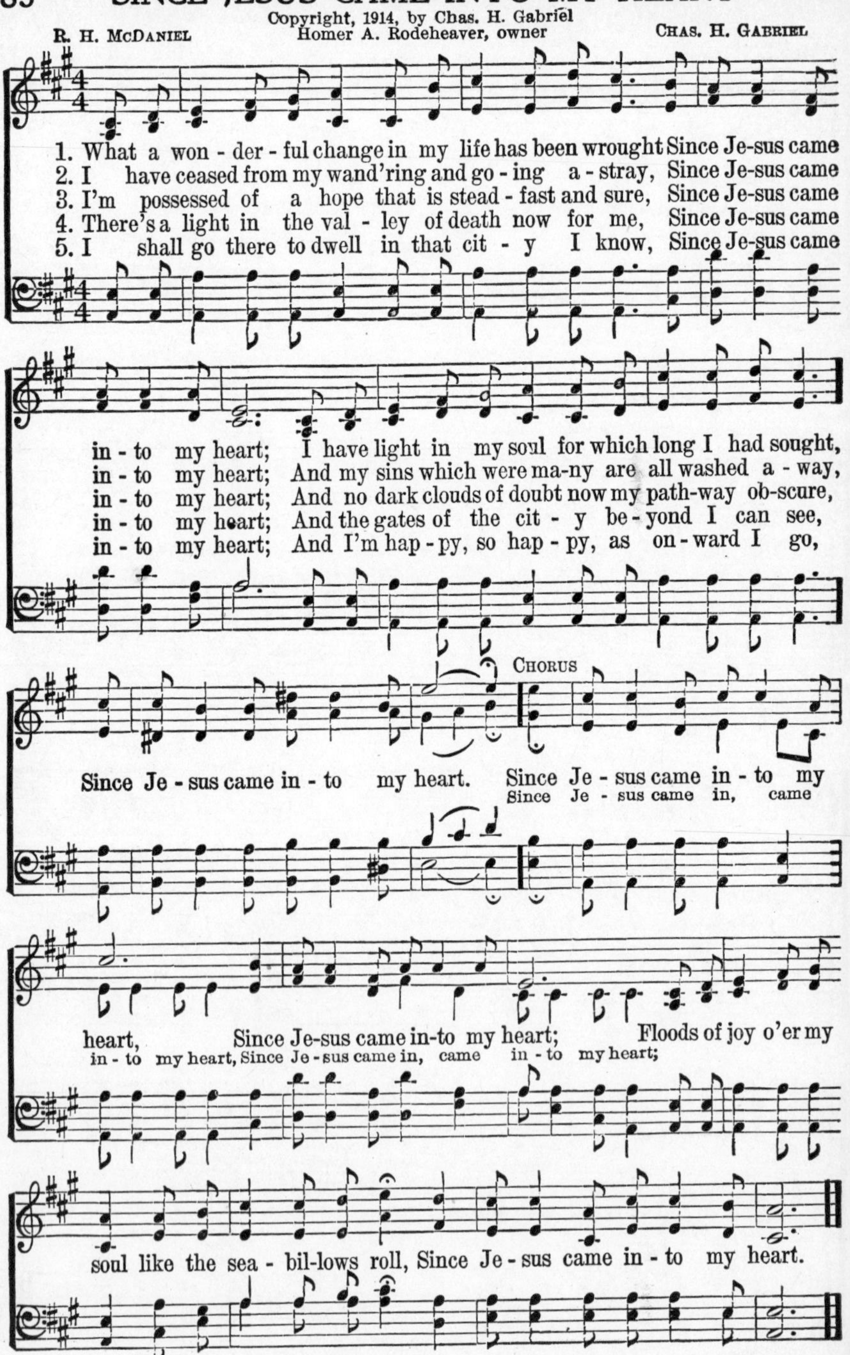
1. What a won - der - ful change in my life has been wrought Since Je-sus came in - to my heart; I have light in my soul for which long I had sought, Since Je - sus came in - to my heart.
2. I have ceased from my wand'ring and go - ing a - stray, Since Je-sus came in - to my heart; And my sins which were ma-ny are all washed a - way,
3. I'm possessed of a hope that is stead - fast and sure, Since Je-sus came in - to my heart; And no dark clouds of doubt now my path-way ob-scure,
4. There's a light in the val - ley of death now for me, Since Je-sus came in - to my heart; And the gates of the cit - y be - yond I can see,
5. I shall go there to dwell in that cit - y I know, Since Je-sus came in - to my heart; And I'm hap - py, so hap - py, as on - ward I go,
CHORUS
Since Je - sus came in - to my heart, Since Je-sus came in-to my heart; Floods of joy o'er my soul like the sea - bil-lows roll, Since Je - sus came in - to my heart.
Since Je - sus came in, came in - to my heart, Since Je - sus came in, came in - to my heart;

TELL ME THE STORY OF JESUS

FANNY J. CROSBY
JNO. R. SWENEY
1. Tell me the sto - ry of Je - sus, Write on my heart ev - 'ry word;
2. Fast-ing a-lone in the des - ert, Tell of the days that are past,
3. Tell of the cross where they nailed Him, Writh-ing in an-guish and pain;
CHO.—Tell me the sto - ry of Je - sus, Write on my heart ev - 'ry word;
FINE
Tell me the sto - ry most pre - cious, Sweet-est that ev - er was heard.
How for our sins He was tempt - ed, Yet was tri - um-phant at last.
Tell of the grave where they laid Him, Tell how He liv - eth a - gain.
Tell me the sto - ry most pre - cious, Sweet - est that ev - er was heard.
Tell how the an - gels, in cho - rus, Sang as they welcomed His birth,
Tell of the years of His la - bor, Tell of the sor - row He bore,
Love in that sto - ry so ten - der, Clear - er than ev - er I see:
D. C. for Chorus
"Glo - ry to God in the high - est! Peace and good ti - dings to earth."
He was de-spised and af - flict - ed, Home-less, de - ject - ed and poor.
Stay, let me weep while you whis - per, Love paid the ran - som for me.

87 ALL HAIL THE POWER OF JESUS' NAME

EDWARD PERRONET — OLIVER HOLDEN

1. All hail the pow'r of Je - sus' name, Let an - gels pros-trate fall;
2. Crown Him, ye morn - ing stars of light, Who fixed this earth - ly ball;
3. Sin - ners, whose love can ne'er for - get The worm-wood and the gall,
4. Let ev - 'ry kin - dred, ev - 'ry tribe On this ter - res - trial ball,
5. O that with yon - der sa - cred throng, We at His feet may fall;

Bring forth the roy - al di - a - dem, And crown Him Lord of all,
Now hail the strength of Israel's might, And crown Him Lord of all,
Go spread your tro-phies at His feet, And crown Him Lord of all,
To Him all maj - es - ty as - cribe, And crown Him Lord of all,
We'll join the ev - er - last - ing song, And crown Him Lord of all,

Bring forth the roy - al di - a - dem, And crown Him Lord of all.
Now hail the strength of Is-rael's might, And crown Him Lord of all.
Go, spread your tro-phies at His feet, And crown Him Lord of all.
To Him all maj - es - ty as-scribe, And crown Him Lord of all.
We'll join the ev - er - last - ing song, And crown Him Lord of all.

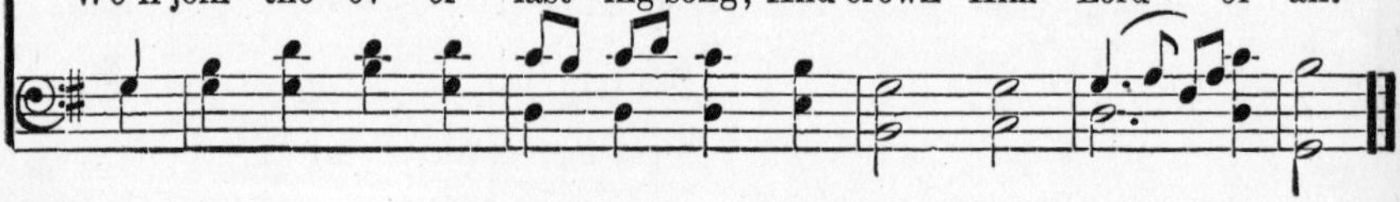

88 BLEST BE THE TIE

JOHN FAWCETT — HANS G. NAEGELI

1. Blest be the tie that binds Our hearts in Christian love; The
2. Be - fore our Fa - ther's throne, We pour our ar - dent pray'rs; Our
3. We share our mu - tual woes, Our mu - tual bur-dens bear; And
4. When we a - sun - der part, It gives us in - ward pain; But

BLEST BE THE TIE

fel - low - ship of kin - dred minds Is like to that a - bove.
fears, our hopes, our aims are one, Our com - forts and our cares.
oft - en for each oth - er flows The sym - pa - thiz - ing tear.
we shall still be joined in heart, And hope to meet a - gain.
89
NEAR THE CROSS
Copyright, 1890, by W. H. Doane. Used by permission
Fanny J. Crosby
W. H. Doane
1. Je - sus, keep me near the cross, There a pre - cious foun - tain
2. Near the cross, a trem-bling soul, Love and mer - cy found me;
3. Near the cross! O Lamb of God, Bring its scenes be - fore me;
4. Near the cross I'll watch and wait, Hop - ing, trust-ing ev - er,
Free to all— a heal - ing stream, Flows from Cal-v'ry's moun - tain.
There the Bright and Morn - ing Star Sheds its beams a - round me.
Help me walk from day to day, With its shad - ows o'er me.
Till I reach the gold - en strand, Just be - yond the riv - er.
Chorus
In the cross, in the cross, Be my glo - ry ev - er;
Till my rap-tured soul shall find Rest be - yond the riv - er.

90 MY ANCHOR HOLDS

"Anchor of the soul, both sure and steadfast."—HEB. 6 : 19

Copyright, 1902-1910. Hope Publishing Co., owner
W. C. MARTIN. Arr.
D. B. TOWNER
1. Though the an - gry sur - ges roll On my tem - pest-driv - en soul,
2. Might - y tides a - bout me sweep, Per - ils lurk with - in the deep,
3. I can feel the an - chor fast As I meet each sud - den blast,
4. Trou - bles al - most 'whelm the soul; Griefs like bil - lows o'er me roll;
I am peace - ful, for I know, Wild - ly though the winds may blow,
An - gry clouds o'er-shade the sky, And the tem - pest ris - es high;
And the ca - ble, though un - seen, Bears the heav - y strain be - tween;
Tempters seek to lure a - stray; Storms ob - scure the light of day:
I've an an - chor safe and sure, That can ev - er-more en - dure.
Still I stand the tem - pest's shock, For my an - chor grips the rock.
Through the storm I safe - ly ride, Till the turn - ing of the tide.
But in Christ I can be - hold, I've an an - chor that shall hold.
CHORUS
And it holds, my an - chor holds; Blow your wild - est, then, O
And it holds,.................. my an - chor holds; Blow your wild - - - est,
gale, On my bark so small and frail: By His grace I shall not
then, O gale,

MY ANCHOR HOLDS
fail, For my an - chor holds, my an - chor holds.
For my an - chor holds, it firm - ly holds,
91
I'LL BE A SUNBEAM
To my grandson, Edwin O. Excell, Jr.
NELLIE TALBOT
Copyright, 1928, by E. O. Excell. Words and music
E. O. EXCELL
1. Je - sus wants me for a sun - beam, To shine for Him each day;......
2. Je - sus wants me to be lov - ing, And kind to all I see; ......
3. I will ask Je - sus to help me To keep my heart from sin; ......
4. I'll be a sun-beam for Je - sus; I can if I but try; ......
In ev - 'ry way try to please Him, At home, at school, at play.......
Show-ing how pleas-ant and hap - py His lit - tle one can be..........
Ev - er re-flect- ing His good - ness, And al - ways shine for Him.......
Serv - ing Him mo-ment by mo - ment, Then live with Him on high.......
CHORUS
A sun - beam, a sun - beam, Je - sus wants me for a sun - beam;
A sun - beam, a sun - beam, I'll be a sun-beam for Him.

92 SAVIOR, MORE THAN LIFE

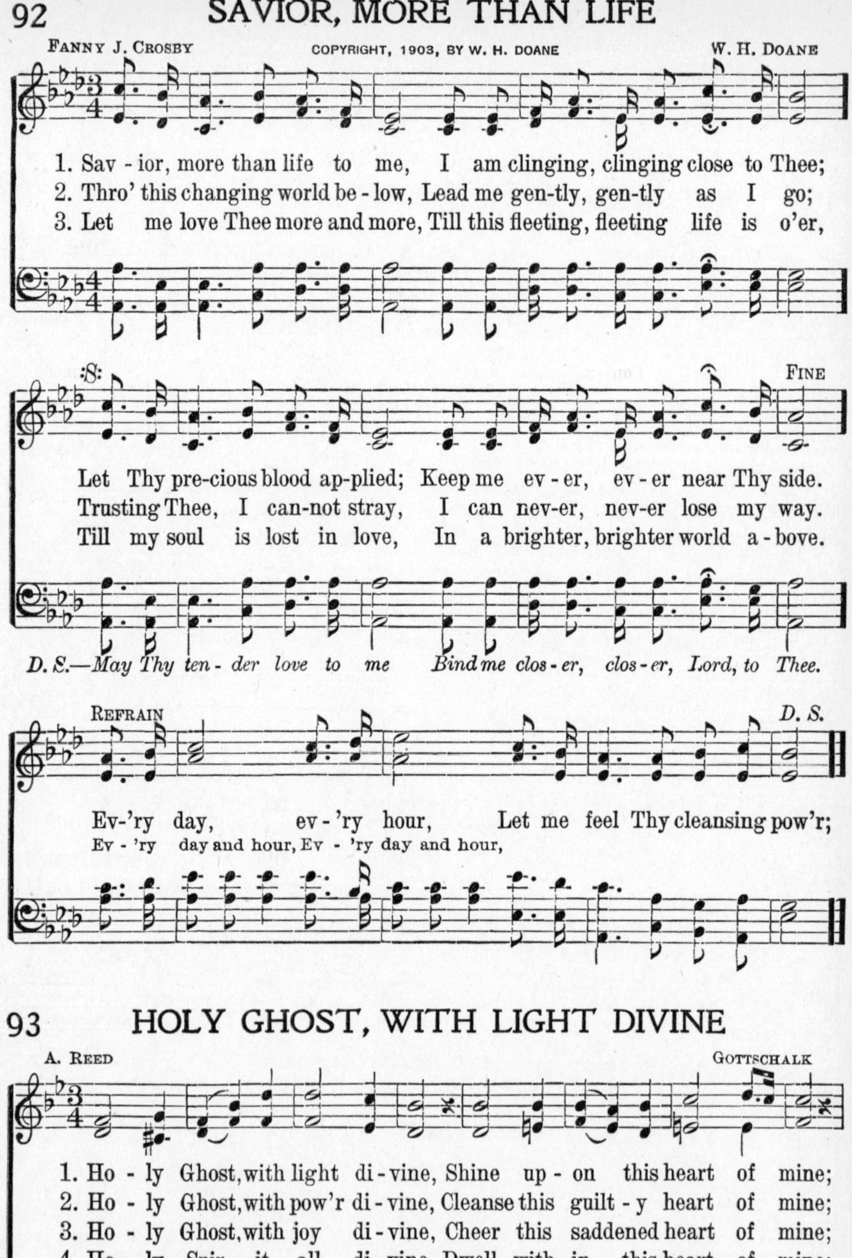
FANNY J. CROSBY
COPYRIGHT, 1903, BY W. H. DOANE
W. H. DOANE
1. Sav - ior, more than life to me, I am clinging, clinging close to Thee;
2. Thro' this changing world be - low, Lead me gen-tly, gen-tly as I go;
3. Let me love Thee more and more, Till this fleeting, fleeting life is o'er,
FINE
Let Thy pre-cious blood ap-plied; Keep me ev - er, ev - er near Thy side.
Trusting Thee, I can-not stray, I can nev-er, nev-er lose my way.
Till my soul is lost in love, In a brighter, brighter world a - bove.
D. S.—May Thy ten - der love to me Bind me clos - er, clos - er, Lord, to Thee.
REFRAIN
D. S.
Ev-'ry day, ev-'ry hour, Let me feel Thy cleansing pow'r;
Ev - 'ry day and hour, Ev - 'ry day and hour,

93 HOLY GHOST, WITH LIGHT DIVINE

A. REED
GOTTSCHALK
1. Ho - ly Ghost, with light di - vine, Shine up - on this heart of mine;
2. Ho - ly Ghost, with pow'r di - vine, Cleanse this guilt - y heart of mine;
3. Ho - ly Ghost, with joy di - vine, Cheer this saddened heart of mine;
4. Ho - ly Spir - it, all di - vine, Dwell with - in this heart of mine;

HOLY GHOST, WITH LIGHT DIVINE

Chase the shades of night a - way, Turn my dark-ness in - to day.
Long hath sin with - out con-trol, Held do - min - ion o'er my soul.
Bid my ma - ny woes de - part, Heal my wounded bleed-ing heart.
Cast down ev - 'ry i - dol throne, Reign supreme and—reign a - lone.
94 BREAK THOU THE BREAD OF LIFE
MARY ANN LATHBURY
WILLIAM F. SHERWIN
1. Break Thou the bread of life, Dear Lord, to me, As Thou didst
2. Bless Thou the Truth, dear Lord, To me— to me— As Thou didst
3. O send Thy Spir - it, Lord, Now un - to me, That He may
4. Thou art the bread of life, O Lord, to me, Thy ho - ly
break the loaves Be - side the sea; Be - yond the sa - cred page
bless the bread By Gal - li - lee; Then shall all bond - age cease,
touch my eyes, And make me see: Show me the truth con-cealed
Word the truth That sav - eth me; Give me to eat and live
I seek Thee, Lord; My spir - it pants for Thee, O Liv - ing Word.
All fet - ters fall; And I shall find my peace, My All in all.
With - in Thy Word, And in Thy book revealed I see the Lord.
With Theee a - bove; Teach me to love Thy truth, For Thou art love.

95 MY MOTHER

Copyright, 1911, by Rodeheaver-Ackley Co.
Homer A. Rodeheaver, owner

Rev. A. H. Ackley — B. D. Ackley

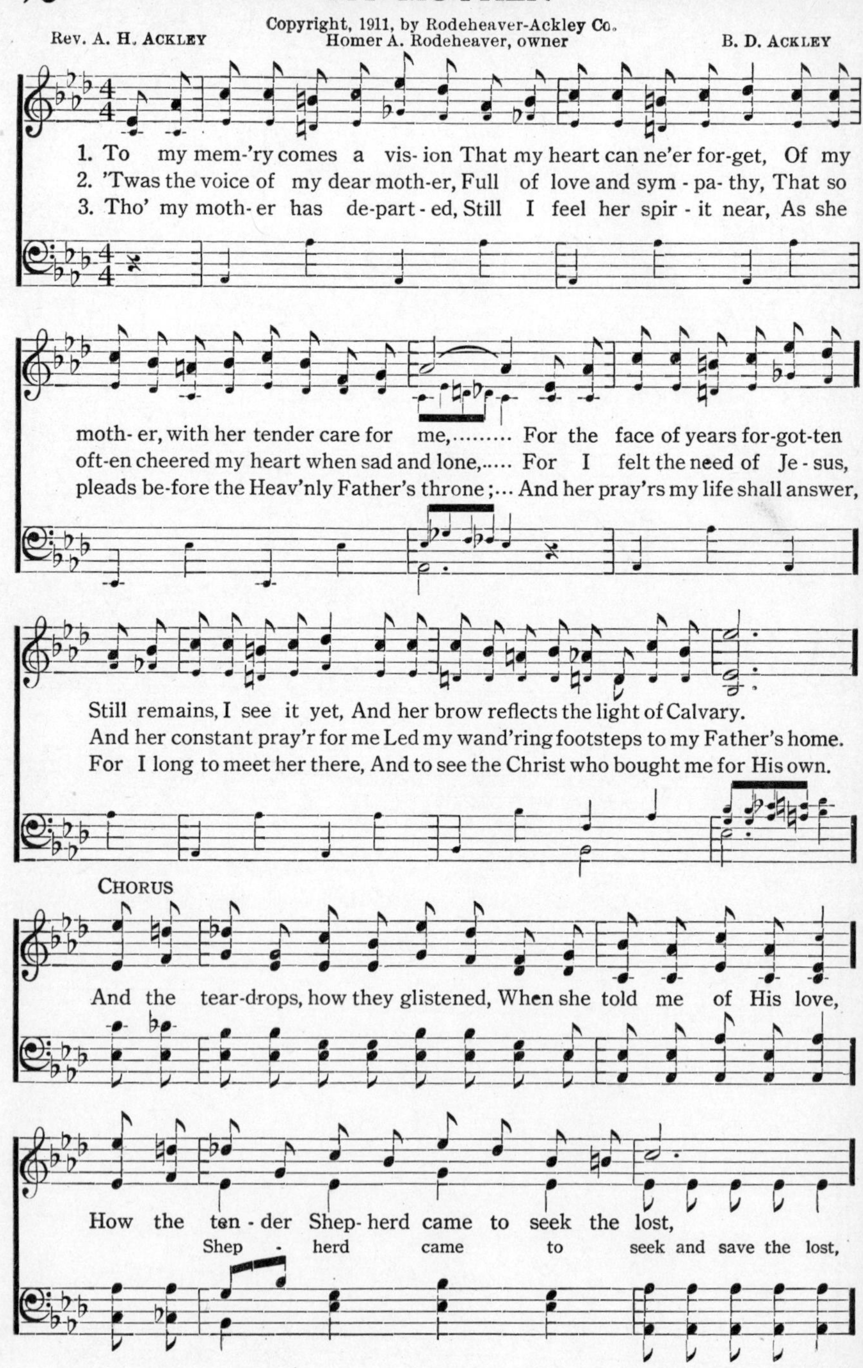
1. To my mem-'ry comes a vis- ion That my heart can ne'er for-get, Of my moth- er, with her tender care for me,......... For the face of years for-got-ten Still remains, I see it yet, And her brow reflects the light of Calvary.
2. 'Twas the voice of my dear moth-er, Full of love and sym - pa- thy, That so oft-en cheered my heart when sad and lone,..... For I felt the need of Je - sus, And her constant pray'r for me Led my wand'ring footsteps to my Father's home.
3. Tho' my moth- er has de-part - ed, Still I feel her spir - it near, As she pleads be-fore the Heav'nly Father's throne;... And her pray'rs my life shall answer, For I long to meet her there, And to see the Christ who bought me for His own.
CHORUS
And the tear-drops, how they glistened, When she told me of His love,
How the ten - der Shep- herd came to seek the lost,
Shep - herd came to seek and save the lost,

MY MOTHER

rit.
O'er the moun-tain, thro' the val - ley, Ev - 'ry foot-print stained with blood,
Till He pur - chased my re - demp - tion on the cross.

96 GRANT US THY PEACE

JOHN ELLERTON ELLERS. 10s. EDWARD J. HOPKINS

1. Sav - ior, a - gain to Thy dear name we raise With one ac - cord our part - ing hymn of praise; We stand to bless Thee ere our wor- ship cease, Then, low - ly kneel - ing, wait Thy word of peace.
2. Grant us Thy peace up - on our homeward way; With Thee be - gan, with Thee shall end the day; Guard Thou the lips from sin, the hearts from shame, That in this house have called up - on Thy name.
3. Grant us Thy peace, Lord, thro' the com-ing night, Turn Thou for us its dark- ness in - to light; From harm and dan - ger keep Thy chil-dren free, For dark and light are both a - like to Thee.
4. Grant us Thy peace throughout our earthly life, Our balm in sor - row, and our stay in strife; Then, when Thy voice shall bid our con- flict cease, Call us, O Lord, to Thine e - ter - nal peace.

97 SUN OF MY SOUL

JOHN KEBLE — PETER RITTER

1. Sun of my soul! Thou Sav-ior dear, It is not night if Thou be near;
Oh, may no earth-born cloud a-rise To hide Thee from Thy servant's eyes!

2. When the soft dews of kind-ly sleep My wea-ry eye-lids gen-tly steep,
Be my last tho't—how sweet to rest For-ev-er on my Savior's breast!

3. A-bide with me from morn till eve, For with-out Thee I can-not live;
A-bide with me when night is nigh, For without Thee I dare not die.

4. Be near to bless me when I wake, Ere thro' the world my way I take;
A-bide with me till in Thy love I lose my-self in heav'n a-bove.

98 HOLY, HOLY, HOLY

REGINALD HEBER — REV. JOHN B. DYKES

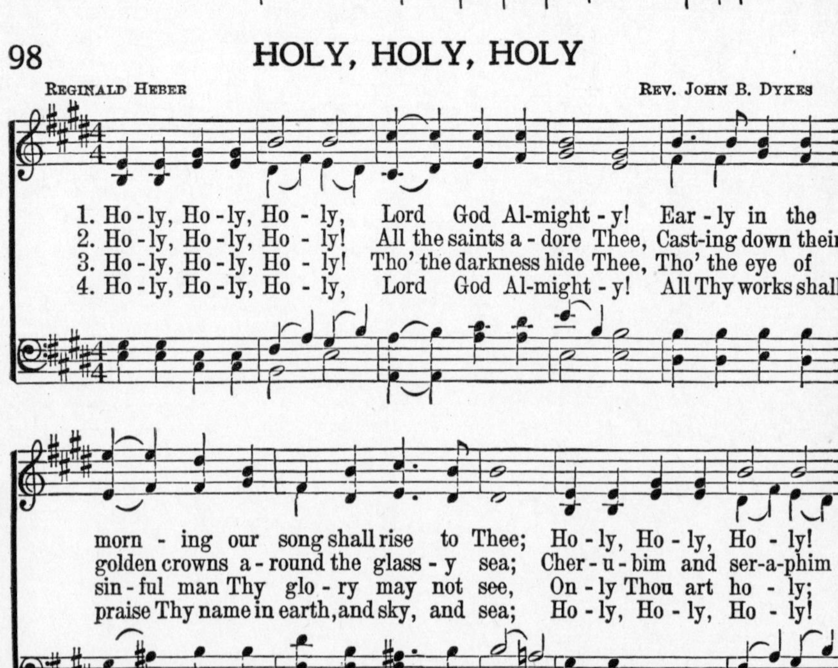
1. Ho-ly, Ho-ly, Ho-ly, Lord God Al-might-y! Ear-ly in the
2. Ho-ly, Ho-ly, Ho-ly! All the saints a-dore Thee, Cast-ing down their
3. Ho-ly, Ho-ly, Ho-ly! Tho' the darkness hide Thee, Tho' the eye of
4. Ho-ly, Ho-ly, Ho-ly, Lord God Al-might-y! All Thy works shall
morn-ing our song shall rise to Thee; Ho-ly, Ho-ly, Ho-ly!
golden crowns a-round the glass-y sea; Cher-u-bim and ser-a-phim
sin-ful man Thy glo-ry may not see, On-ly Thou art ho-ly;
praise Thy name in earth, and sky, and sea; Ho-ly, Ho-ly, Ho-ly!

HOLY, HOLY, HOLY
Mer - ci-ful and Might - y! God in Three Per-sons, bless-ed Trin - i - ty!
fall - ing down be-fore Thee, Who wert, and art, and ev - er-more shalt be.
there is none be - side Thee Per - fect in pow'r, in love, and pu - ri - ty.
Mer - ci-ful and Might - y! God in Three Per-sons, bless-ed Trin - i - ty!
99
SWEET HOUR OF PRAYER
W. W. WALFORD
WM. B. BRADBURY
1. Sweet hour of pray'r! sweet hour of pray'r! That calls me from a world of care,
2. Sweet hour of pray'r! sweet hour of pray'r! Thy wings shall my pe - ti - tion bear
3. Sweet hour of pray'r! sweet hour of pray'r! May I thy con - so - la - tion share,
And bids me at my Father's throne Make all my wants and wish - es known;
To Him whose truth and faith - ful-ness En-gage the wait - ing soul to bless;
Till, from Mount Pisgah's loft - y height, I view my home, and take my flight:
In sea - sons of dis-tress and grief, My soul has oft - en found re - lief,
And since He bids me seek His face, Be-lieve His word and trust His grace,
This robe of flesh I'll drop and rise To seize the ev - er - last - ing prize;
And oft escaped the tempter's snare By thy re-turn, sweet hour of pray'r.
I'll cast on Him my ev - 'ry care, And wait for thee, sweet hour of pray'r.
And shout, while passing thro' the air, Farewell, farewell, sweet hour of pray'r.

100 THE OLD-FASHIONED MEETING

H. B. — Herbert Buffum

1. Oh, how well I re - mem-ber in the old-fash - ioned days, When some
2. There was singing, such sing-ing, of those old-fash - ioned airs! There was
3. Well, they say it is better, "Things have changed, don't you know," And the
4. If the Lord nev - er chang-es, as the fashions of men, If He's

old - fash - ioned peo - ple had some old - fash - ioned ways; In the
pow - er, such pow - er in those old - fash - ioned pray'rs, An old -
peo - ple in gen - 'ral, seem to think it is so; And they
al - ways the same, why, He is old - fash - ioned, then! As an

old - fash-ioned meet-ings, as they tar - ried there, In the old - fash-ioned
fashioned con - vic - tion made the sin - ner pray, And the Lord heard and
call me old - fash-ioned when I dare to say, That I like it far
old - fash-ioned sin - ner saved thro' old-time grace, Oh, I'm sure He will

man - ner, how God an-swered their pray'r.
saved Him, in the old - fash - ioned way.
bet - ter in the old - fash - ioned way.
take me to an old - fash - ioned place.

CHORUS.

'Twas an old-fash-ioned meeting, in an old-fash-ioned place, Where some old - fash-ioned peo - ple had some

old-fash-ioned grace: As an old-fash-ioned sin-ner I be-gan to
pray, And God heard me, and saved me in the old fash-ioned way.

101 JESUS LOVES ME

(The favorite Hymn of China)

WILLIAM B. BRADBURY

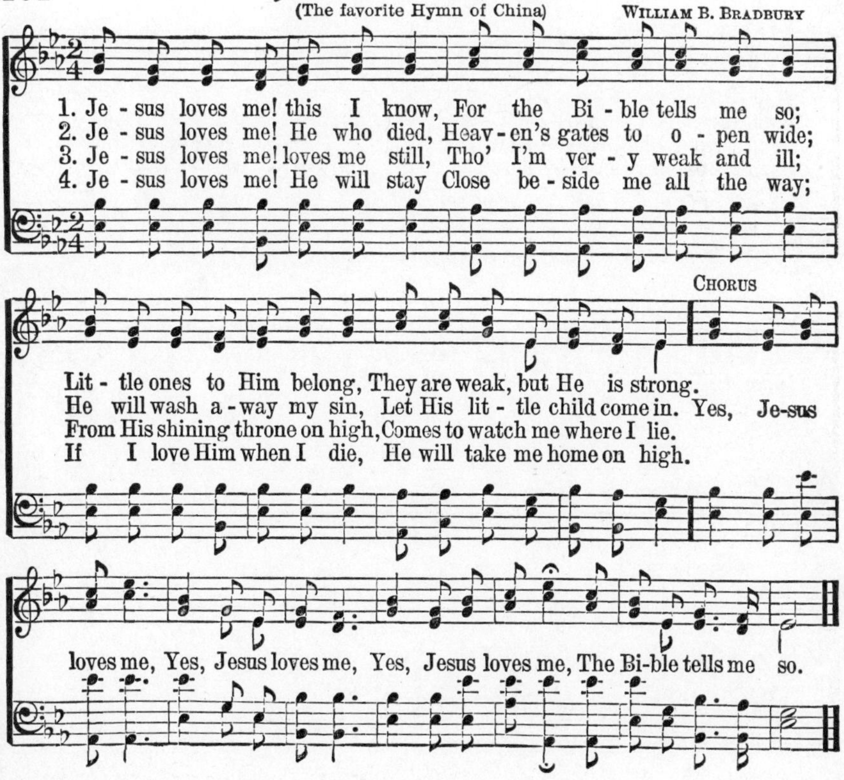

1. Je - sus loves me! this I know, For the Bi - ble tells me so;
2. Je - sus loves me! He who died, Heav - en's gates to o - pen wide;
3. Je - sus loves me! loves me still, Tho' I'm ver - y weak and ill;
4. Je - sus loves me! He will stay Close be - side me all the way;

Lit - tle ones to Him belong, They are weak, but He is strong.
He will wash a - way my sin, Let His lit - tle child come in.
From His shining throne on high, Comes to watch me where I lie.
If I love Him when I die, He will take me home on high.

CHORUS

Yes, Je-sus loves me, Yes, Jesus loves me, Yes, Jesus loves me, The Bi-ble tells me so.

THE KINGDOM IS COMING

MARY B. C. SLADE — ROBERT M. McINTOSH

1. From all the dark pla - ces Of earth's hea-then ra - ces, O see how the thick shadows fly! The voice of sal - va - tion A - wakes ev - 'ry na - tion, "Come o - ver and help us," they cry.
2. The sun - light is glanc - ing O'er ar - mies ad - vanc - ing To con - quer the king - doms of sin; Our Lord shall pos-sess them, His pres - ence shall bless them, His beau - ty shall en - ter them in.
3. With shout - ing and sing - ing, And ju - bi - lant ring - ing, Their arms of re - bel - lion cast down, At last ev - 'ry na - tion, The Lord of sal - va - tion Their King and Re - deem - er shall crown!
REFRAIN
The kingdom is coming, O tell ye the story, God's banner ex-alt-ed shall be!
The earth shall be full of His knowledge and glory, As waters that cover the sea!

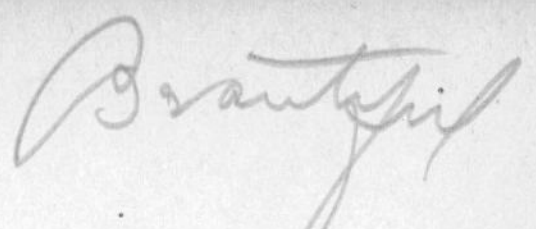

103 IN THE GARDEN

C. A. M. — C. Austin Miles

1. I come to the gar-den a - lone, While the dew is still on the ros - es; And the voice I hear, Fall-ing on my ear; The Son of God dis - clos - es.

2. He speaks, and the sound of His voice Is so sweet the birds hush their sing - ing, And the mel - o - dy That He gave to me, With - in my heart is ring - ing.

3. I'd stay in the gar-den with Him Tho' the night a-round me be fall - ing, But He bids me go; Thro' the voice of woe, His voice to me is call - ing.

CHORUS

And He walks with me, and He talks with me, And He tells me I am His own, And the joy we share as we tar - ry there, None other has ev - er known.

104 ROCK OF AGES
Augustus M. Toplady
Thomas Hastings
1. Rock of A - ges, cleft for me, Let me hide my - self in Thee;
2. Could my tears for - ev - er flow, Could my zeal no lan-guor know,
3. While I draw this fleet - ing breath, When my eyes shall close in death,
Let the wa - ter and the blood, From Thy wound - ed side which flowed,
These for sin could not a - tone; Thou must save, and Thou a - lone:
When I rise to worlds unknown, And be - hold Thee on Thy throne,
Be of sin the dou - ble cure, Save from wrath and make me pure.
In my hand no price I bring, Sim - ply to Thy cross I cling.
Rock ot A - ges, cleft for me, Let me hide my - self in Thee.
105 NEARER, MY GOD, TO THEE
Sarah F. Adams
Arr. by Lowell Mason
1. Near - er, my God, to Thee, Near - er to Thee! E'en though it
2. Though like the wan - der - er, The sun gone down, Dark - ness be
3. There let the way ap - pear, Steps un - to heav'n: All that Thou
4. Then, with my wak - ing tho'ts Bright with Thy praise, Out of my
5. Or if on joy - ful wing, Cleav - ing the sky, Sun, moon, and

NEARER, MY GOD, TO THEE
be a cross That rais - eth me; Still all my song shall be,
o - ver me, My rest a stone; Yet in my dreams I'd be
send - est me, In mer - cy giv'n: An - gels to beck - on me,
sto - ny griefs Beth - el I'll raise; So by my woes to be
stars for - got, Up - wards I'll fly, Still all my song shall be,
Near - er, my God, to Thee, Near - er, my God, to Thee, Nearer, to Thee!
106
JESUS, LOVER OF MY SOUL
CHARLES WESLEY
S. B. MARSH
FINE
1. Je - sus, Lov - er of my soul, Let me to Thy bos - om fly,
While the near - er wa - ters roll, While the tem - pest still is high!
2. Oth - er ref - uge have I none; Hangs my help - less soul on Thee:
Leave, ah, leave me not a - lone, Still sup - port and com - fort me!
3. Thou, O Christ, art all I want; More than all in Thee I find;
Raise the fall - en, cheer the faint, Heal the sick, and lead the blind.
4. Plenteous grace with Thee is found, Grace to cov - er all my sin;
Let the heal - ing streams abound, Make and keep me pure with - in.
D. C.–Safe in - to the ha - ven guide, O re - ceive my soul at last!
D. C.–Cov - er my de - fense - less head With the shad - ow of Thy wing.
D. C.–False and full of sin I am, Thou art full of truth and grace.
D. C.–Spring Thou up with - in my heart, Rise to all e - ter - ni - ty.
D.C.
Hide me, O my Sav - ior, hide, Till the storm of life is past;
All my trust on Thee is stayed, All my help from Thee I bring;
Just and ho - ly is Thy name, I am all un - right - eous - ness;
Thou of life the foun - tain art; Free - ly let me take of Thee;

107 AWAY IN A MANGER

M. L.
Martin Luther
1. A - way in a man-ger, No crib for a bed, The lit - tle Lord
2. The cat - tle are low - ing, The Ba - by a - wakes, But lit - tle Lord
3. Be near me, Lord Je - sus, I ask Thee to stay Close by me for-
Je - sus Laid down His sweet head; The stars in the sky Looked
Je - sus, No cry - ing He makes; I love Thee, Lord Je - sus! Look
ev - er, And love me, I pray; Bless all the dear chil-dren In
down where He lay,—The lit - tle Lord Je - sus, A - sleep on the hay.
down from the sky, And stay by my cra-dle, Till morn-ing is nigh.
Thy ten-der care, And take us to heav-en, To live with Thee there.
108 WHEN HE COMETH
Rev. W. O. Cushing
Geo. F. Root
1. When He com-eth, when He com-eth To make up His jew-els, All His
2. He will gath-er, He will gath-er The gems for His kingdom, All the
3. Lit - tle chil-dren, lit - tle chil-dren Who love their Re-deem-er, Are the
Chorus
jew - els, pre-cious jew-els, His loved and His own.
pure ones, all the bright ones, His loved and His own. Like the stars of the morning,
jew - els, pre-cious jew-els, His loved and His own.

WHEN HE COMETH
His bright crown adorning, They shall shine in their beauty, Bright gems for His crown.
109 I THINK WHEN I READ THAT SWEET STORY
Jemima Luke, 1841
SWEET STORY
Traditional English Melody
1. I think when I read that sweet sto - ry of old, When
2. I wish that His hands had been placed on my head, That His
3. Yet still to His foot - stool in prayer I may go, And
4. But thou - sands and thou-sands who wan - der and fall Nev - er
5. I long for the joy of that glo - ri - ous time, The
Je - sus was here a-mong men, How He called lit - tle chil - dren as
arm had been thrown a-round me, And that I might have seen His kind
ask for a share in His love; And if I now ear - nest - ly
heard of that heav - en - ly home; I should like them to know there is
sweet-est and bright-est and best, When the dear lit - tle chil - dren of
lambs to His fold, I should like to have been with them then.
look when He said, "Let the lit - tle ones come un - to Me."
seek Him be - low, I shall see Him and hear Him a - bove.
room for them all, And that Je - sus has bid them to come.
ev - er - y clime Shall crowd to His arms and be blest. A-MEN.

110 I'M A PILGRIM

Copyright, 1911, by Rodeheaver & Herbert
Homer A. Rodeheaver, owner

Mrs. S. B. Dana — J. B. Herbert

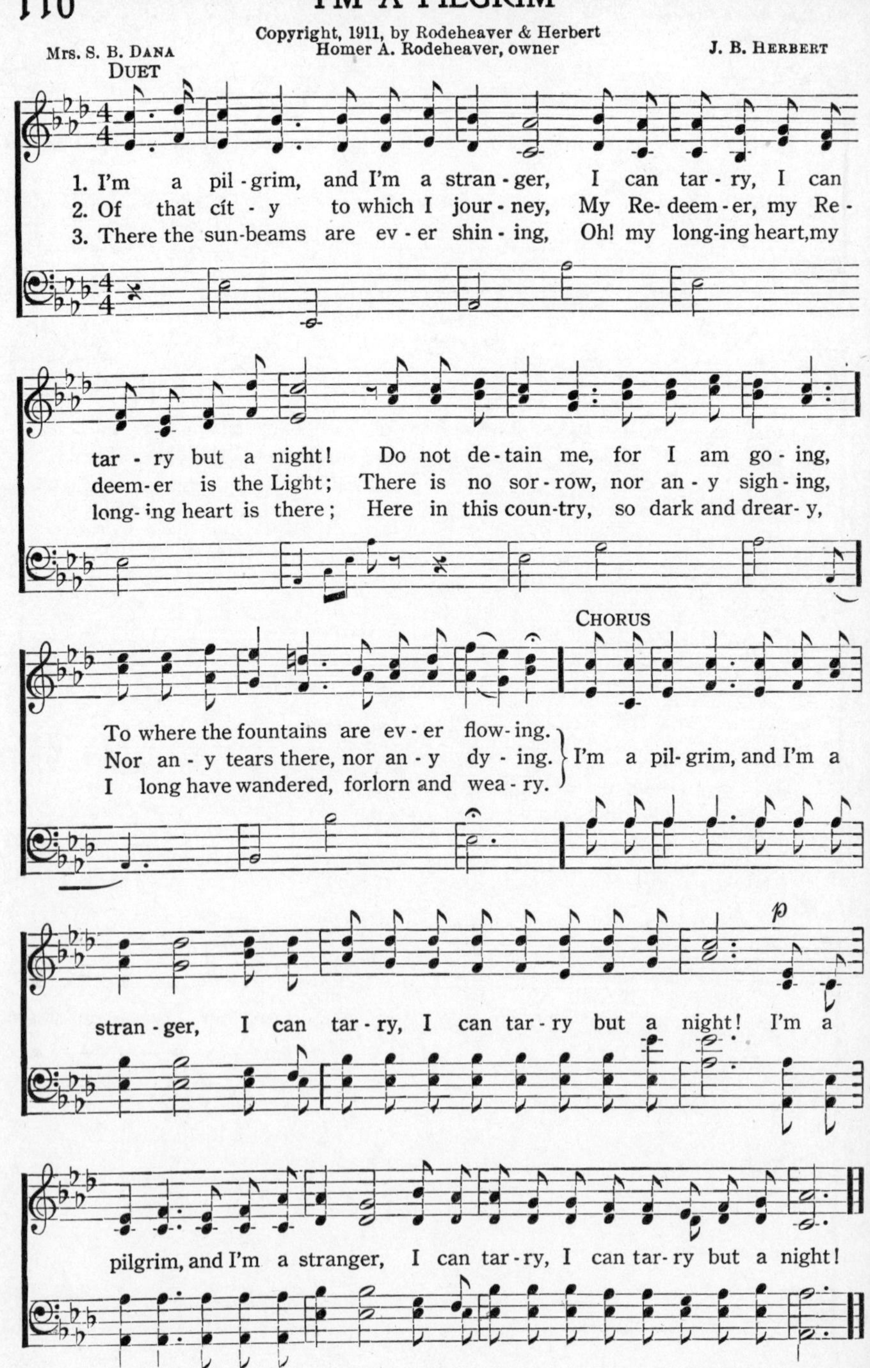
DUET
1. I'm a pil-grim, and I'm a stran-ger, I can tar-ry, I can tar-ry but a night! Do not de-tain me, for I am go-ing, To where the fountains are ev-er flow-ing.
2. Of that cít-y to which I jour-ney, My Re-deem-er, my Re-deem-er is the Light; There is no sor-row, nor an-y sigh-ing, Nor an-y tears there, nor an-y dy-ing.
3. There the sun-beams are ev-er shin-ing, Oh! my long-ing heart, my long-ing heart is there; Here in this coun-try, so dark and drear-y, I long have wandered, forlorn and wea-ry.
CHORUS
I'm a pil-grim, and I'm a stran-ger, I can tar-ry, I can tar-ry but a night! I'm a pilgrim, and I'm a stranger, I can tar-ry, I can tar-ry but a night!
p

111 RING THE BELLS OF HEAVEN

Rev. W. O. Cushing — G. F. Root

Joyfully
1. Ring the bells of heav-en! there is joy to-day, For a soul re-turn-ing from the wild! See! the Fa-ther meets him out up-on the way, Wel-com-ing His wea-ry, wan-d'ring child.
2. Ring the bells of heav-en! there is joy to-day, For the wan-d'rer now is rec-on-ciled; Yes, a soul is res-cued from his sin-ful way, And is born a-new a ran-somed child.
3. Ring the bells of heav-en! spread the feast to-day! An-gels, swell the glad tri-um-phant strain! Tell the joy-ful ti-dings, bear it far a-way! For a pre-cious soul is born a-gain.
Chorus
Glo-ry! glo-ry! how the an-gels sing; Glo-ry! glo-ry! how the loud harps ring! 'Tis the ran-somed ar-my, like a might-y sea, Peal-ing forth the an-them of the free.

112 MY REDEEMER

P. P. Bliss — James McGranahan

1. I will sing of my Re-deem-er, And His won-drous love to me;
2. I will tell the won-drous sto-ry, How my lost es-tate to save,
3. I will praise my dear Re-deem-er, His tri-um-phant pow'r I'll tell,
4. I will sing of my Re-deem-er, And His heav'n-ly love to me;
On the cru-el cross He suf-fered, From the curse to set me free.
In His bound-less love and mer-cy, He the ran-som free-ly gave.
How the vic-to-ry He giv-eth O-ver sin, and death, and hell.
He from death to life hath bro't me, Son of God with Him to be.
CHORUS
Sing, oh, sing . . . . of my Re-deem - er,
of my Re-deem-er, Sing, oh, sing of my Re-deem-er,
With His blood . . . . He pur-chased me, ...
He pur-chased me, With His blood He pur-chased me,
On the cross . . . . He sealed my par - don,
He sealed my par-don, On the cross He sealed my par-don,

MY REDEEMER

Paid the debt, ... and made me free. . . . .
and made me free,
and made me free.

113 TAKE THE NAME OF JESUS WITH YOU

Mrs. Lydia Baxter
W. H. Doane

1. Take the name of Je-sus with you, Child of sor-row and of woe;
It will joy and com-fort give you, Take it, then, wher-e'er you go.

2. Take the name of Je-sus ev-er, As a shield from ev-'ry snare;
If temp-ta-tions round you gath-er, Breathe that ho-ly name in prayer.

3. O the precious name of Je-sus! How it thrills our souls with joy,
When His lov-ing arms re-ceive us, And His songs our tongues em-ploy!

4. At the name of Je-sus bow-ing, Fall-ing pros-trate at His feet,
King of kings in Heav'n we'll crown Him, When our jour-ney is com-plete.

CHORUS

Pre-cious name, (Precious name,) O how sweet! (O how sweet!) Hope of earth and joy of Heav'n;
Pre-cious name, O how sweet!... (Precious name, O how sweet, how sweet!) Hope of earth and joy of Heav'n.

114 MEMORIES OF GALILEE
ROBERT MORRIS
H. R. PALMER
1. Each coo-ing dove............... and sigh-ing bough,........... That makes the eve........... so blest to me,........... Has something far........... di-vin - er now,.............. It bears me back........... to Gal - i - lee...............
2. Each flow'ry glen............... and moss- y dell, ... Where hap - py birds......... in song a - gree,.......... Thro' sun-ny morn......... the prais-es tell................ Of sights and sounds......... in Gal - i - lee...............
3. And when I read .... the thrilling lore................ Of Him who walked...... up - on the sea,........... I long, oh, how.......... I long once more........... To fol - low Him........... in Gal - i - lee...............
CHORUS
O Gal - i - lee! sweet Gal - i - lee! Where Je - sus loved so much to be;
O Gal - i - lee! blue Gal - i - lee! Come, sing thy song a-gain to me!
sing thy song a - gain to me!

115 SAFE IN THE ARMS OF JESUS

FANNY J. CROSBY — Copyright, property of Fannie T. Doane — W. H. DOANE

1. Safe in the arms of Je - sus, Safe on His gen - tle breast, There by His love o'er - shad - ed, Sweet-ly my soul shall rest. Hark! 'tis the voice of an - gels, Borne in a song to me, O - ver the fields of glo - ry, O - ver the jas - per sea.........
2. Safe in the arms of Je - sus, Safe from cor-rod - ing care, Safe from the world's temp-ta - tions, Sin can-not harm me there. Free from the blight of sor - row, Free from my doubts and fears; On - ly a few more tri - als, On - ly a few more tears!.....
3. Je - sus, my heart's dear ref - uge, Je - sus has died for me; Firm on the Rock of A - ges, Ev - er my trust shall be. Here let me wait with pa - tience, Wait till the night is o'er; Wait till I see the morn - ing Break on the gold - en shore......
CHORUS
Safe in the arms of Je - sus, Safe on His gen - tle breast, There by His love o'er - shad - ed, Sweetly my soul shall rest.

THE HOME OVER THERE

D. W. C. HUNTINGTON — T. C. O'Kane, owner of copyright — TULLIUS C. O'KANE.

1. Oh! think of the home over there, By the side of the riv - er of light,
2. Oh! think of the friends over there, Who before us the journey have trod,
3. My Sav- ior is now o-ver there, There my kindred and friends are at rest,
4. I'll soon be at home o-ver there, For the end of my journey I see;

o-ver there,

Where the saints, all immortal and fair, Are robed in their garments of white.
Of the songs that they breathe on the air, In their home in the palace of God.
Then a-way from my sorrow and care, Let me fly to the land of the blest.
Man - y dear to my heart, o-ver there, Are watching and waiting for me.

over there.

O- ver there, o - ver there, Oh! think of the home o- ver there,
Oh! think of the friends over there,
My Sav - ior is now o - ver there,
Over there, over there, I'll soon be at home o - ver there,

over there,

O- ver there, o - ver there, o-ver there, Oh! think of the home o - ver there.
Oh! think of the friends over there.
My Sav - ior is now o - ver there.
O-ver there, I'll soon be at home o - ver there,

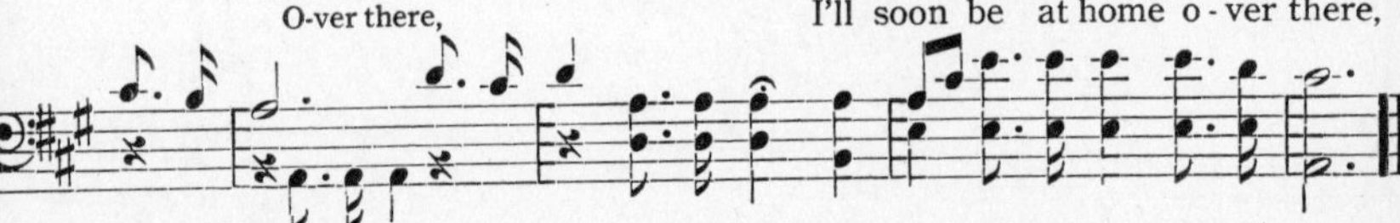

117 THROW OUT THE LIFE-LINE

E. S. UFFORD
E. S. UFFORD. Arr. by GEO. C. STEBBINS
1. Throw out the Life-Line a-cross the dark wave, There is a broth-er whom some one should save; Some-bod-y's broth-er! oh, who then will dare To throw out the Life-Line, his per-il to share?
2. Throw out the Life-Line with hand quick and strong; Why do you tar-ry, why lin-ger so long? See! he is sink-ing; oh, has-ten to-day— And out with the Life-Boat! a-way, then, a-way!
3. Throw out the Life-Line to danger-fraught men, Sink-ing in an-guish where you've nev-er been; Winds of temp-ta-tion and bil-lows of woe Will soon hurl them out where the dark wa-ters flow.
4. Soon will the sea-son of res-cue be o'er, Soon will they drift to e-ter-ni-ty's shore, Haste then, my broth-er, no time for de-lay, But throw out the Life-Line and save them to-day.
CHORUS
Throw out the Life-Line! Throw out the Life-Line! Someone is drift-ing a-way; Throw out the Life-Line! Throw out the Life-Line! Some-one is sink-ing to-day.

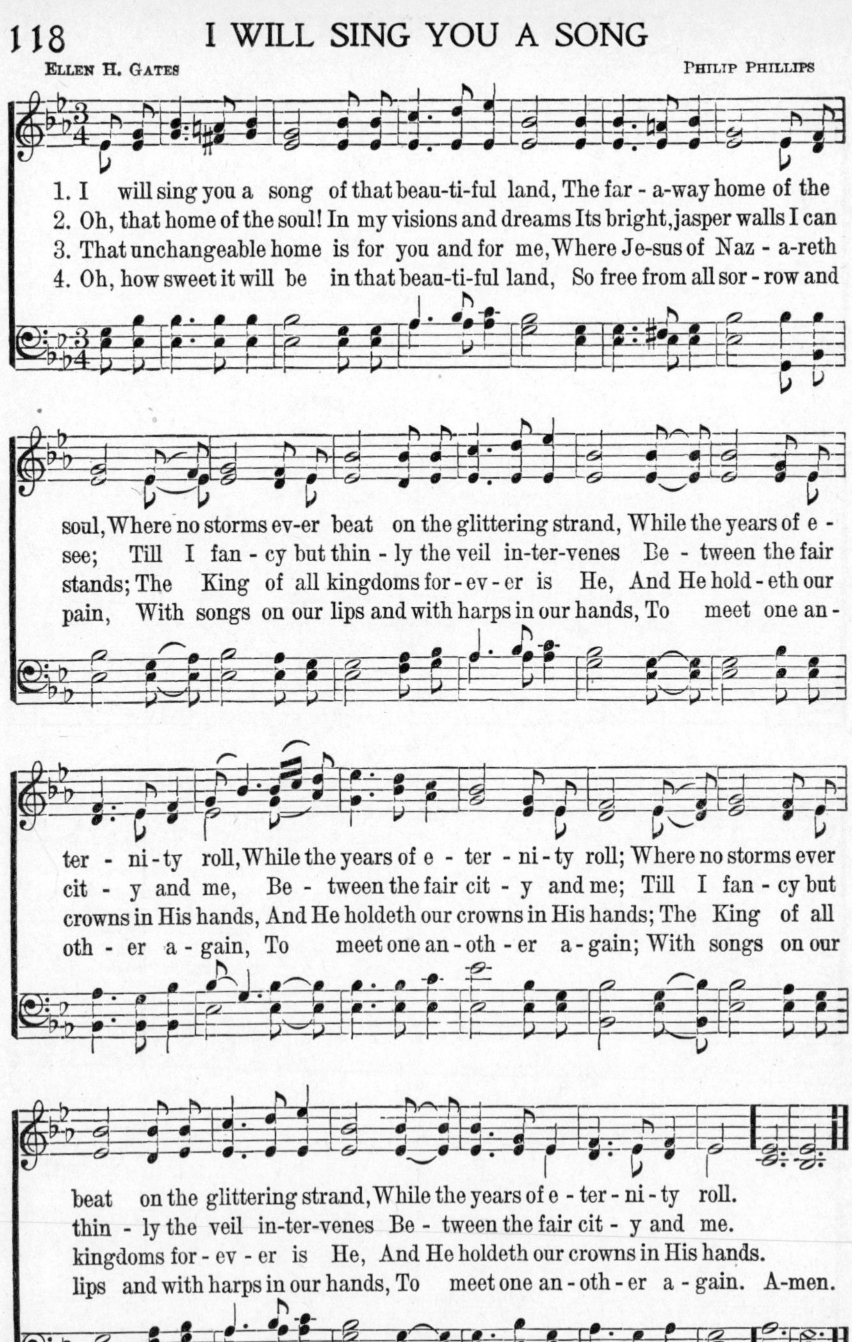
118 I WILL SING YOU A SONG
Ellen H. Gates
Philip Phillips
1. I will sing you a song of that beau-ti-ful land, The far - a-way home of the
2. Oh, that home of the soul! In my visions and dreams Its bright, jasper walls I can
3. That unchangeable home is for you and for me, Where Je-sus of Naz - a-reth
4. Oh, how sweet it will be in that beau-ti-ful land, So free from all sor - row and
soul, Where no storms ev-er beat on the glittering strand, While the years of e -
see; Till I fan - cy but thin - ly the veil in-ter-venes Be - tween the fair
stands; The King of all kingdoms for - ev - er is He, And He hold - eth our
pain, With songs on our lips and with harps in our hands, To meet one an -
ter - ni - ty roll, While the years of e - ter - ni - ty roll; Where no storms ever
cit - y and me, Be - tween the fair cit - y and me; Till I fan - cy but
crowns in His hands, And He holdeth our crowns in His hands; The King of all
oth - er a - gain, To meet one an - oth - er a - gain; With songs on our
beat on the glittering strand, While the years of e - ter - ni - ty roll.
thin - ly the veil in-ter-venes Be - tween the fair cit - y and me.
kingdoms for - ev - er is He, And He holdeth our crowns in His hands.
lips and with harps in our hands, To meet one an - oth - er a - gain. A-men.

119 IT IS WELL WITH MY SOUL

H. G. Spafford
P. P. Bliss
1. When peace, like a river, attendeth my way, When sorrows like sea-billows roll; Whatever my lot, Thou hast taught me to say, It is well, it is well with my soul.
2. Though Satan should buffet, tho' trials should come, Let this blest assurance control, That Christ has regarded my helpless estate, And hath shed His own blood for my soul.
3. My sin—oh, the bliss of this glorious tho't—My sin—not in part, but the whole, Is nailed to the cross and I bear it no more, Praise the Lord, praise the Lord, O my soul!
4. And, Lord, haste the day when the faith shall be sight, The clouds be rolled back as a scroll, The trump shall resound and the Lord shall descend, "Even so"—it is well with my soul.
Chorus
It is well . . . . . with my soul, ... It is well, it is well with my soul.
It is well with my soul,

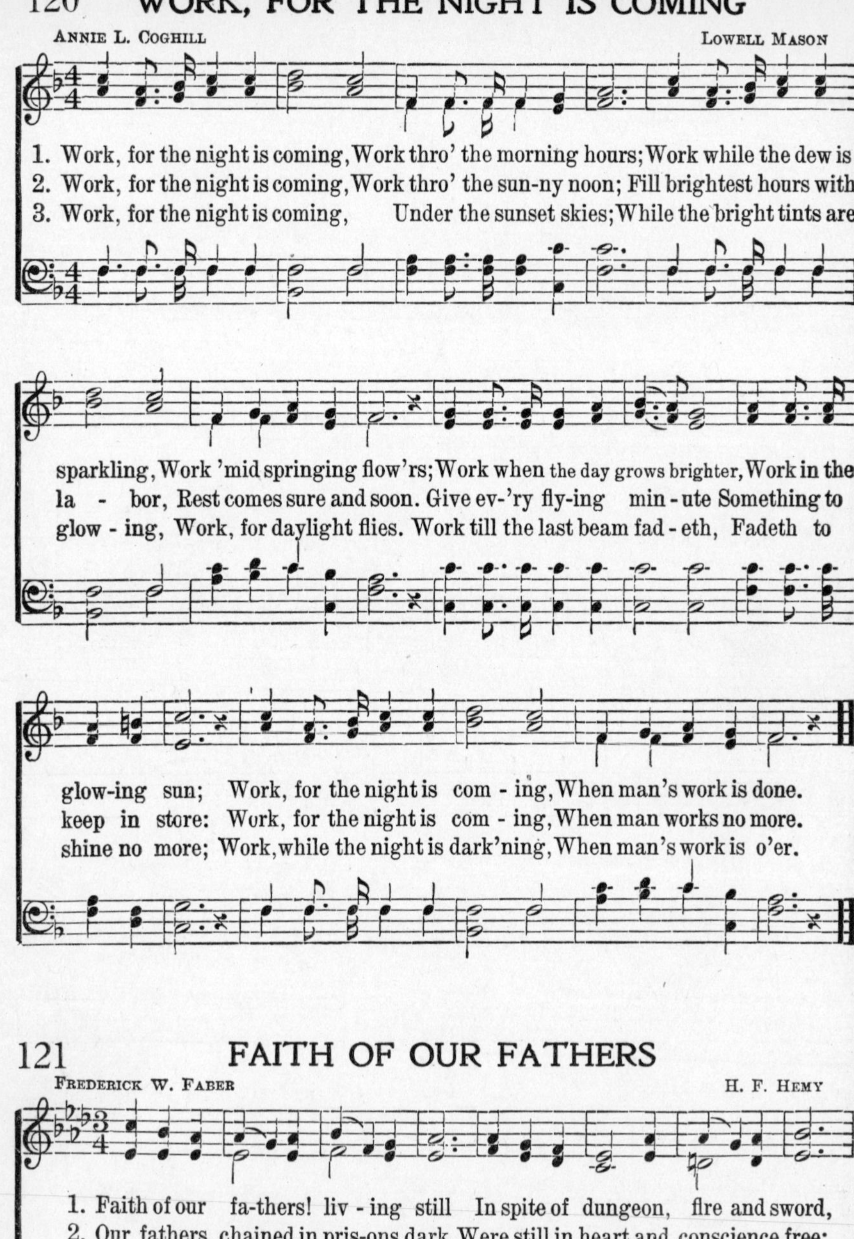
120 WORK, FOR THE NIGHT IS COMING
Annie L. Coghill
Lowell Mason
1. Work, for the night is coming, Work thro' the morning hours; Work while the dew is sparkling, Work 'mid springing flow'rs; Work when the day grows brighter, Work in the glowing sun; Work, for the night is coming, When man's work is done.
2. Work, for the night is coming, Work thro' the sun-ny noon; Fill brightest hours with la - bor, Rest comes sure and soon. Give ev-'ry fly-ing min-ute Something to keep in store: Work, for the night is com - ing, When man works no more.
3. Work, for the night is coming, Under the sunset skies; While the bright tints are glow - ing, Work, for daylight flies. Work till the last beam fad - eth, Fadeth to shine no more; Work, while the night is dark'ning, When man's work is o'er.
121 FAITH OF OUR FATHERS
Frederick W. Faber
H. F. Hemy
1. Faith of our fa-thers! liv - ing still In spite of dungeon, fire and sword,
2. Our fathers, chained in pris-ons dark, Were still in heart and conscience free:
3. Faith of our fa-thers! we will love Both friend and foe in all our strife:

FAITH OF OUR FATHERS
O how our hearts beat high with joy Whene'er we hear that glo - rious word!
How sweet would be their children's fate, If they, like them, could die for thee!
And preach thee, too, as love knows how, By kind-ly words and vir - tuous life:
Faith of our fa-thers! ho - ly faith! We will be true to thee till death!
Faith of our fa-thers! ho - ly faith! We will be true to thee till death!
Faith of our fa-thers! ho - ly faith! We will be true to thee till death!
122
STAND UP FOR JESUS
G. DUFFIELD
G. J. WEBB
1. Stand up, stand up for Je - sus, Ye soldiers of the cross, Lift high His
2. Stand up, stand up for Je - sus, The trumpet call o - bey; Forth to the
3. Stand up, stand up for Je - sus—Stand in His strength alone; The arm of
roy - al ban-ner, It must not suf-fer loss. From vic-t'ry un-to vic-t'ry, His
might-y con-flict, In this His glorious day. "Ye that are men now serve Him," A -
flesh will fail you—Ye dare not trust your own; Put on the gos-pel ar-mor, And,
ar - my shall He lead, Till ev - 'ry foe is vanquished And Christ is Lord indeed.
gainst unnumbered foes; Let courage rise with danger, And strength to strength oppose.
watching un-to pray'r, Where du-ty calls, or dan-ger, Be nev-er wanting there.

123 THE HAVEN OF REST

H. L. Gilmour — Used by per. Dr. H. L. Gilmour — George D. Moore

1. My soul in sad exile was out on life's sea, So burdened with sin and distressed, Till I heard a sweet voice saying, "Make me your choice;" And I entered the "Haven of Rest."

2. I yielded myself to His tender embrace, And faith taking hold of the Word, My fetters fell off, and I anchored my soul; The "Haven of Rest" is my Lord.

3. The song of my soul, since the Lord made me whole, Has been the old story so blest, Of Jesus who'll save whosoever will have A home in the "Haven of Rest."

4. How precious the tho't that we all may recline, Like John the beloved and blest, On Jesus' strong arm, where no tempest can harm, Secure in the "Haven of Rest."

5. O come to the Savior, He patiently waits To save by His power divine; Come, anchor your soul in the "Haven of Rest," And say, "My Beloved is mine."

CHORUS

I've anchored my soul in the "Haven of Rest," I'll sail the wide seas no more; The tempest may sweep o'er the wild stormy deep; In Jesus I'm safe evermore.

124 SHALL WE GATHER AT THE RIVER

Robert Lowry
Robert Lowry
1. Shall we gath-er at the riv - er, Where bright an-gel feet have trod;
2. On the bo - som of the riv - er, Where the Sav-iour-King we own;
3. Ere we reach the shining riv - er, Lay we ev - 'ry bur - den down;
4. Soon we'll reach the shining riv - er, Soon our pil-grim-age will cease;
With its crys-tal tide, for - ev - er Flow-ing by the throne of God.
We shall meet, and sorrow nev - er 'Neath the glo - ry of the throne.
Grace our spir - its will de - liv - er, And pro-vide a robe and crown.
Soon our hap - py hearts will quiv - er With the mel - o - dy of peace.
Refrain
Yes, we'll gath-er at the riv - er, The beau-ti-ful, the beau-ti - ful riv - er,
Gath-er with the saints at the riv - er That flows by the throne of God.

125 COME, HOLY SPIRIT, HEAVENLY DOVE

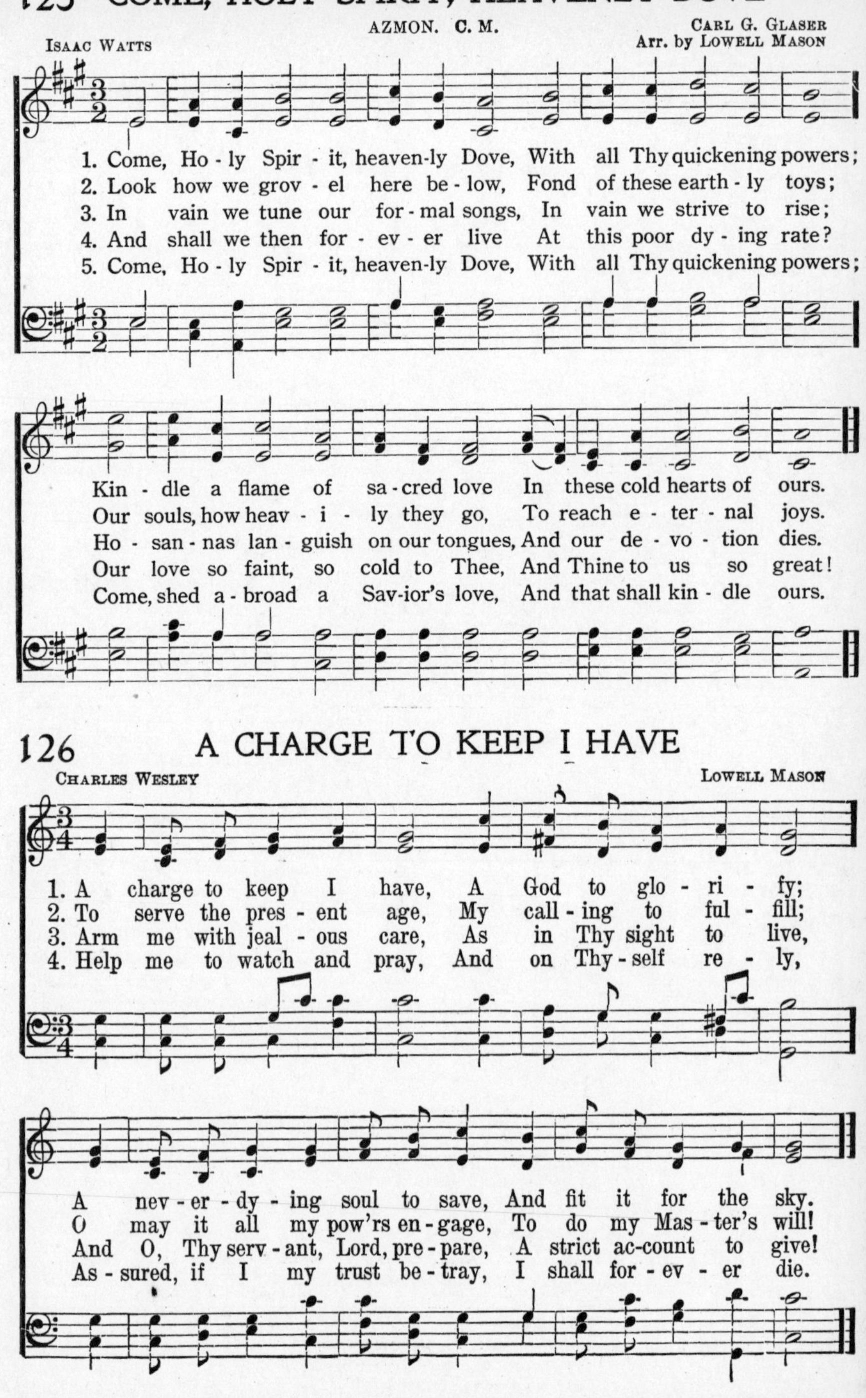
AZMON. C. M.
Carl G. Glaser
Isaac Watts
Arr. by Lowell Mason
1. Come, Ho - ly Spir - it, heaven-ly Dove, With all Thy quickening powers;
2. Look how we grov - el here be - low, Fond of these earth - ly toys;
3. In vain we tune our for - mal songs, In vain we strive to rise;
4. And shall we then for - ev - er live At this poor dy - ing rate?
5. Come, Ho - ly Spir - it, heaven-ly Dove, With all Thy quickening powers;
Kin - dle a flame of sa - cred love In these cold hearts of ours.
Our souls, how heav - i - ly they go, To reach e - ter - nal joys.
Ho - san - nas lan - guish on our tongues, And our de - vo - tion dies.
Our love so faint, so cold to Thee, And Thine to us so great!
Come, shed a - broad a Sav-ior's love, And that shall kin - dle ours.
126 A CHARGE TO KEEP I HAVE
Charles Wesley
Lowell Mason
1. A charge to keep I have, A God to glo - ri - fy;
2. To serve the pres - ent age, My call - ing to ful - fill;
3. Arm me with jeal - ous care, As in Thy sight to live,
4. Help me to watch and pray, And on Thy - self re - ly,
A nev - er - dy - ing soul to save, And fit it for the sky.
O may it all my pow'rs en - gage, To do my Mas - ter's will!
And O, Thy serv - ant, Lord, pre - pare, A strict ac-count to give!
As - sured, if I my trust be - tray, I shall for - ev - er die.

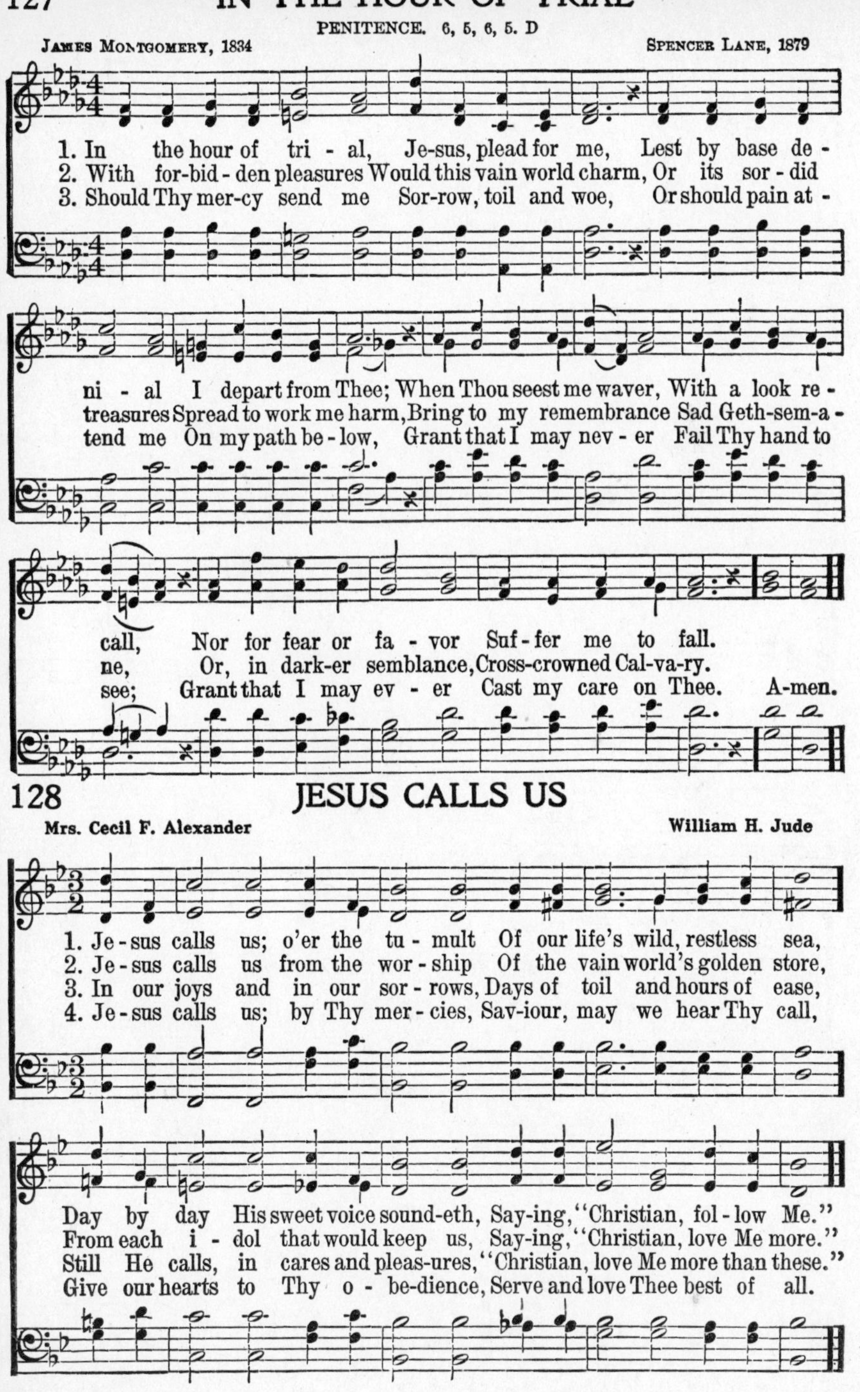
127 IN THE HOUR OF TRIAL
PENITENCE. 6, 5, 6, 5. D
James Montgomery, 1834
Spencer Lane, 1879
1. In the hour of tri - al, Je-sus, plead for me, Lest by base de - ni - al I depart from Thee; When Thou seest me waver, With a look re - call, Nor for fear or fa - vor Suf - fer me to fall.
2. With for-bid - den pleasures Would this vain world charm, Or its sor - did treasures Spread to work me harm, Bring to my remembrance Sad Geth-sem-a - ne, Or, in dark-er semblance, Cross-crowned Cal-va-ry.
3. Should Thy mer-cy send me Sor-row, toil and woe, Or should pain at - tend me On my path be - low, Grant that I may nev - er Fail Thy hand to see; Grant that I may ev - er Cast my care on Thee. A-men.
128 JESUS CALLS US
Mrs. Cecil F. Alexander
William H. Jude
1. Je - sus calls us; o'er the tu - mult Of our life's wild, restless sea, Day by day His sweet voice sound-eth, Say-ing, "Christian, fol - low Me."
2. Je - sus calls us from the wor - ship Of the vain world's golden store, From each i - dol that would keep us, Say-ing, "Christian, love Me more."
3. In our joys and in our sor - rows, Days of toil and hours of ease, Still He calls, in cares and pleas-ures, "Christian, love Me more than these."
4. Je - sus calls us; by Thy mer - cies, Sav-iour, may we hear Thy call, Give our hearts to Thy o - be-dience, Serve and love Thee best of all.

129 DWELLING IN BEULAH LAND

C. A. M. | C. AUSTIN MILES

1. Far a-way the noise of strife up - on my ear is fall - ing, Then I know the
2. Far be-low the storm of doubt up- on the world is beat- ing, Sons of men in
3. Let the storm-y breez-es blow, their cry can-not a - larm me, I am safe-ly
4. Viewing here the works of God, I sink in con-tem- pla- tion, Hear-ing now His

sins of earth be - set on ev - 'ry hand; Doubt and fear and things of earth in
bat - tle long the en - e - my with - stand; Safe am I with - in the cas - tle
shelter'd here, pro-tect - ed by God's hand; Here the sun is al-ways shin-ing,
bless- ed voice, I see the way He plann'd; Dwell-ing in the Spir - it, here I

vain to me are call - ing, None of these shall move me from Beu - lah Land.
of God's word re - treat- ing, Nothing there can reach me—'tis Beu - lah Land.
here there's naught can harm me, I am safe for - ev - er in Beu - lah Land.
learn of full sal - va - tion, Glad - ly will I tar - ry in Beu - lah Land.

CHORUS

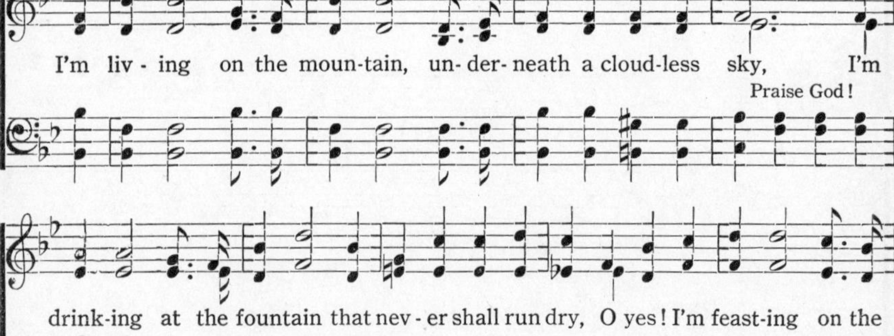
I'm liv - ing on the moun-tain, un- der- neath a cloud-less sky, I'm
Praise God!
drink-ing at the fountain that nev - er shall run dry, O yes! I'm feast-ing on the

DWELLING IN BEULAH LAND
man - na from a boun - ti - ful sup - ply For I am dwelling in Beu - lah Land.
130 HOW FIRM A FOUNDATION
GEORGE KEITH
Unknown
1. How firm a foun - da - tion, ye saints of the Lord, Is laid for your
2. "Fear not, I am with thee, O be not dis - mayed, For I am thy
3. "When thro' the deep wa - ters I call thee to go, The riv - ers of
4. "When thro' fier - y tri - als thy path - way shall lie, My grace, all - suf -
faith in His ex - cel - lent Word! What more can He say than to
God, I will still give thee aid; I'll strength - en thee, help thee, and
sor - row shall not o - ver - flow; For I will be with thee thy
fi - cient, shall be thy sup - ply, The flames shall not hurt thee: I
you He hath said, To you, who for ref - uge to Je - sus have
cause thee to stand, Up - held by My gra - cious, om - nip - o - tent
tri - als to bless, And sanc - ti - fy to thee thy deep - est dis -
on - ly de - sign Thy dross to con - sume, and thy gold to re -
fled? To you, who for ref - uge to Je - sus have fled?
hand, Up - held by My gra - cious, om - nip - o - tent hand.
tress, And sanc - ti - fy to thee thy deep - est dis - tress.
fine, Thy dross to con - sume, and thy gold to re - fine."

131 GLORIOUS THINGS OF THEE ARE SPOKEN

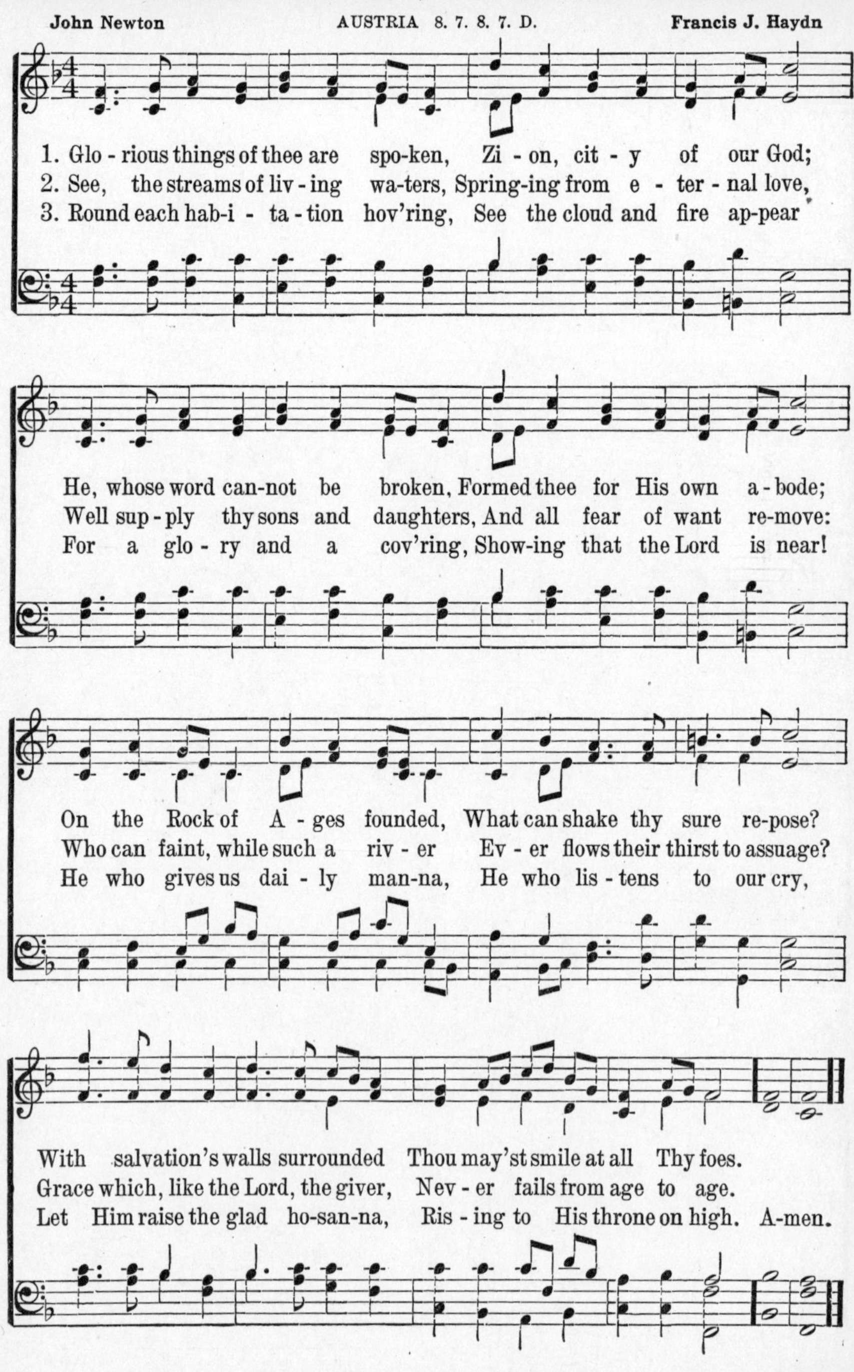
John Newton
AUSTRIA 8. 7. 8. 7. D.
Francis J. Haydn
1. Glo - rious things of thee are spo-ken, Zi - on, cit - y of our God;
2. See, the streams of liv - ing wa-ters, Spring-ing from e - ter - nal love,
3. Round each hab-i - ta - tion hov'ring, See the cloud and fire ap-pear
He, whose word can-not be broken, Formed thee for His own a - bode;
Well sup - ply thy sons and daughters, And all fear of want re-move:
For a glo - ry and a cov'ring, Show-ing that the Lord is near!
On the Rock of A - ges founded, What can shake thy sure re-pose?
Who can faint, while such a riv - er Ev - er flows their thirst to assuage?
He who gives us dai - ly man-na, He who lis - tens to our cry,
With salvation's walls surrounded Thou may'st smile at all Thy foes.
Grace which, like the Lord, the giver, Nev - er fails from age to age.
Let Him raise the glad ho-san-na, Ris - ing to His throne on high. A-men.

132 GUIDE ME, O THOU GREAT JEHOVAH

William Williams — Thomas Hastings

1. Guide me, O Thou great Je - ho - vah, Pil - grim thro' this bar - ren
2. O - pen now the crys - tal fount - ain Whence the heal - ing wa - ters
3. When I tread the verge of Jor - dan, Bid my anx - ious fears sub -
land; I am weak, but Thou art might - y, Hold me with Thy pow'r-ful
flow; Let the fi - ery, cloud - y pil - lar Lead me all my jour - ney
side; Bear me thro' the swell - ing cur - rent, Land me safe on Ca-naan's
hand; Bread of heav - en, Feed me till I want no more;
thro'; Strong De - liv - 'rer, Be Thou still my Strength and Shield;
side: Songs of prais - es I will ev - er give to Thee;
Bread of heav - en, Feed me till I want no more.
Strong De - liv - 'rer, Be Thou still my Strength and Shield.
Songs of prais - es I will ev - er give to Thee.

133 THERE IS ROOM IN MY HEART FOR THEE.
Emily E. S. Elliott
ELLIOTT. P. M.
Timothy R. Matthews
1. Thou didst leave Thy throne and Thy kingly crown, When Thou camest to earth for me;
2. Heaven's arch-es rang when the an - gels sang, Pro - claiming Thy roy - al de-gree;
3. The fox-es found rest, and the birds their nest In the shade of the for - est tree;
4. Thou cam - est, O Lord, with the living word, That should set Thy peo - ple free;
5. When heaven's arches ring, and her choirs shall sing At Thy coming to vic - to - ry,
But in Beth-le-hem's home there was found no room For Thy ho - ly na - tiv - i - ty.
But in low - ly birth didst Thou come to earth, And in great hu - mil - i - ty.
But Thy couch was the sod, O Thou Son of God, In the des - erts of Gal - i - lee.
But with mocking scorn and with crown of thorn, They bore Thee to Cal - va - ry.
Let Thy voice call me home, saying, "Yet there is room, There is room at my side for Thee."
O come to my heart, Lord Je - sus! There is room in my heart for Thee.
O come to my heart, Lord Je - sus! There is room in my heart for Thee.
O come to my heart, Lord Je - sus! There is room in my heart for Thee.
O come to my heart, Lord Je - sus! Thy cross is my on - ly plea.
And my heart shall rejoice, Lord Je - sus, When Thou comest and call'st for me. A-men.
134 LEAD, KINDLY LIGHT
John H. Newman
John B. Dykes
1. Lead, kindly Light, amid th'encircling gloom, Lead Thou me on! The night is
2. I was not ever thus, nor prayed that Thou Shouldst lead me on; I loved to
3. So long Thy pow'r hath blest me, sure it still Will lead me on O'er moor and

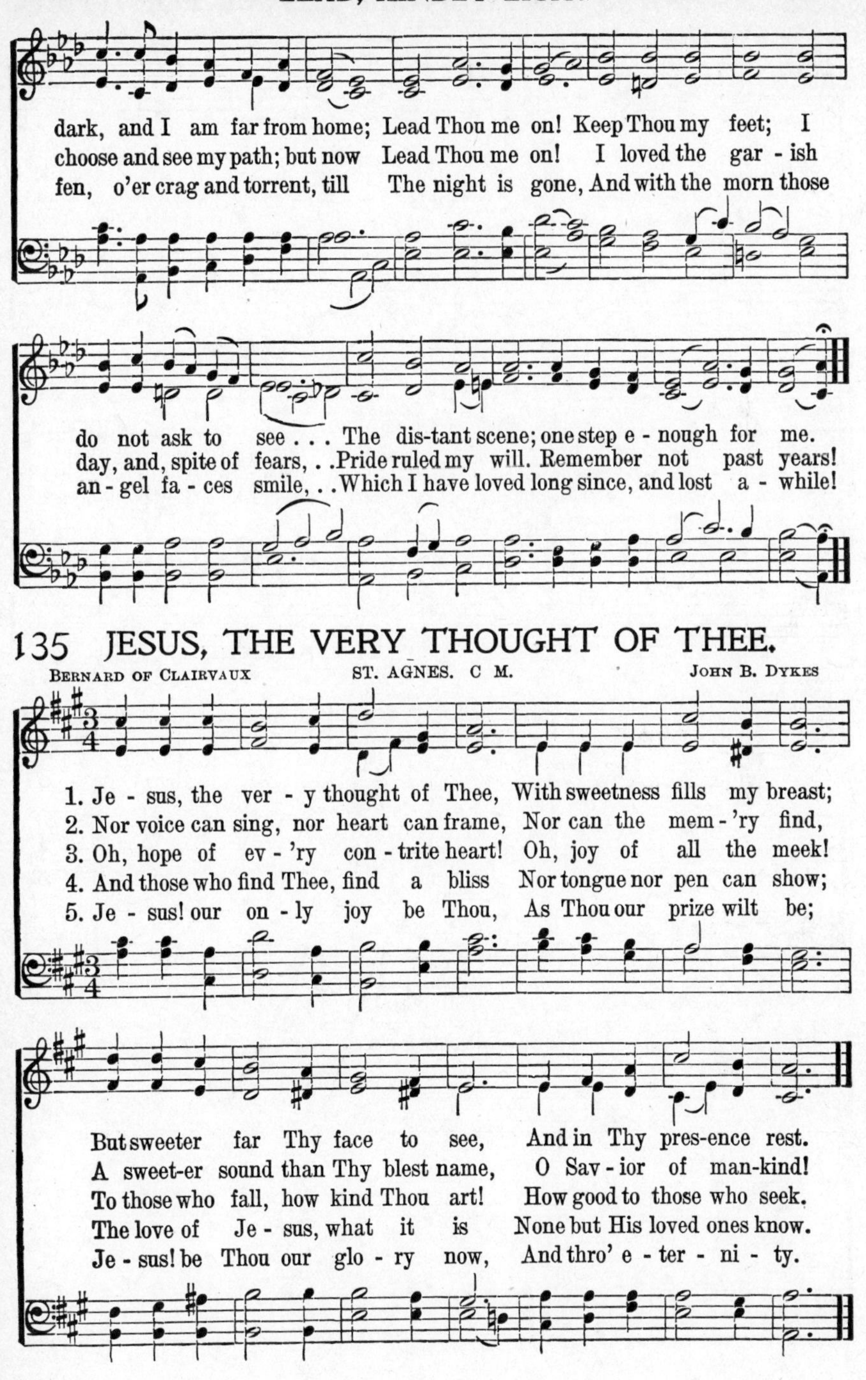
dark, and I am far from home; Lead Thou me on! Keep Thou my feet; I
choose and see my path; but now Lead Thou me on! I loved the gar - ish
fen, o'er crag and torrent, till The night is gone, And with the morn those
do not ask to see . . . The dis-tant scene; one step e - nough for me.
day, and, spite of fears, . . Pride ruled my will. Remember not past years!
an - gel fa - ces smile, . . Which I have loved long since, and lost a - while!
135 JESUS, THE VERY THOUGHT OF THEE.
BERNARD OF CLAIRVAUX
ST. AGNES. C M.
JOHN B. DYKES
1. Je - sus, the ver - y thought of Thee, With sweetness fills my breast;
2. Nor voice can sing, nor heart can frame, Nor can the mem - 'ry find,
3. Oh, hope of ev - 'ry con - trite heart! Oh, joy of all the meek!
4. And those who find Thee, find a bliss Nor tongue nor pen can show;
5. Je - sus! our on - ly joy be Thou, As Thou our prize wilt be;
But sweeter far Thy face to see, And in Thy pres-ence rest.
A sweet-er sound than Thy blest name, O Sav - ior of man-kind!
To those who fall, how kind Thou art! How good to those who seek.
The love of Je - sus, what it is None but His loved ones know.
Je - sus! be Thou our glo - ry now, And thro' e - ter - ni - ty.

136 ARE YOU COMING HOME TO-NIGHT?

S. M. J. JAMES McGRANAHAN

1. Are you com-ing Home, ye wand-'rers, Whom Je-sus died to win,
2. Are you com-ing Home, ye lost ones? Be-hold your Lord doth wait:
3. Are you com-ing Home, ye guilt-y, Who bear the load of sin?
4. Are you com-ing Home, ye wea-ry, Who long for rest and peace?
All foot-sore, lame and wea-ry, Your gar-ments stain'd with sin?
Come, then, no lon-ger lin-ger, Come ere it be too late;
Out-side you've long been stand-ing, Come now and ven-ture in;
Your bur-den has been heav-y, And long you've sought re-lease;
Will you seek the blood of Je-sus, To wash your gar-ments white?
Will you come and let Him save you? Oh! trust His lov' and might;
Will you heed the Sav-ior's prom-ise, And dare to trus. Him quite?
Will you now ac-cept of Je-sus, In Him your heart de-light?
Will you trust His pre-cious prom-ise, Are you com-ing Home to-night?
Will you come while He is call-ing, Are you com-ing Home to-night?
"Come un-to me," saith Je-sus; Are you com-ing Home to-night?
Will you ful-ly yield up to Him, Are you com-ing Home to-night?
CHORUS
Are you com-ing Home to-night? Are you com-ing Home to-night?

ARE YOU COMING HOME TO-NIGHT?

1
Are you coming Home to Jesus, Out of darkness into light?
2
To your loving, heav'nly Father, Are you coming Home to-night?

137 TAKE TIME TO BE HOLY

W. D. LONGSTAFF GEO. C. STEBBINS

1. Take time to be holy, Speak oft with thy Lord; Abide in Him always, And feed on His Word. Make friends of God's children; Help those who are weak; Forgetting in nothing His blessing to seek.
2. Take time to be holy, The world rushes on; Spend much time in secret With Jesus alone. By looking to Jesus, Like Him thou shalt be; Thy friends in thy conduct His likeness shall see.
3. Take time to be holy, Let Him be thy Guide; And run not before Him, Whatever betide; In joy or in sorrow, Still follow thy Lord, And, looking to Jesus, Still trust in His Word.
4. Take time to be holy, Be calm in thy soul; Each tho't and each motive Beneath His control; Thus led by His Spirit To fountains of love, Thou soon shalt be fitted For service above.

138 O LOVE THAT WILT NOT LET ME GO

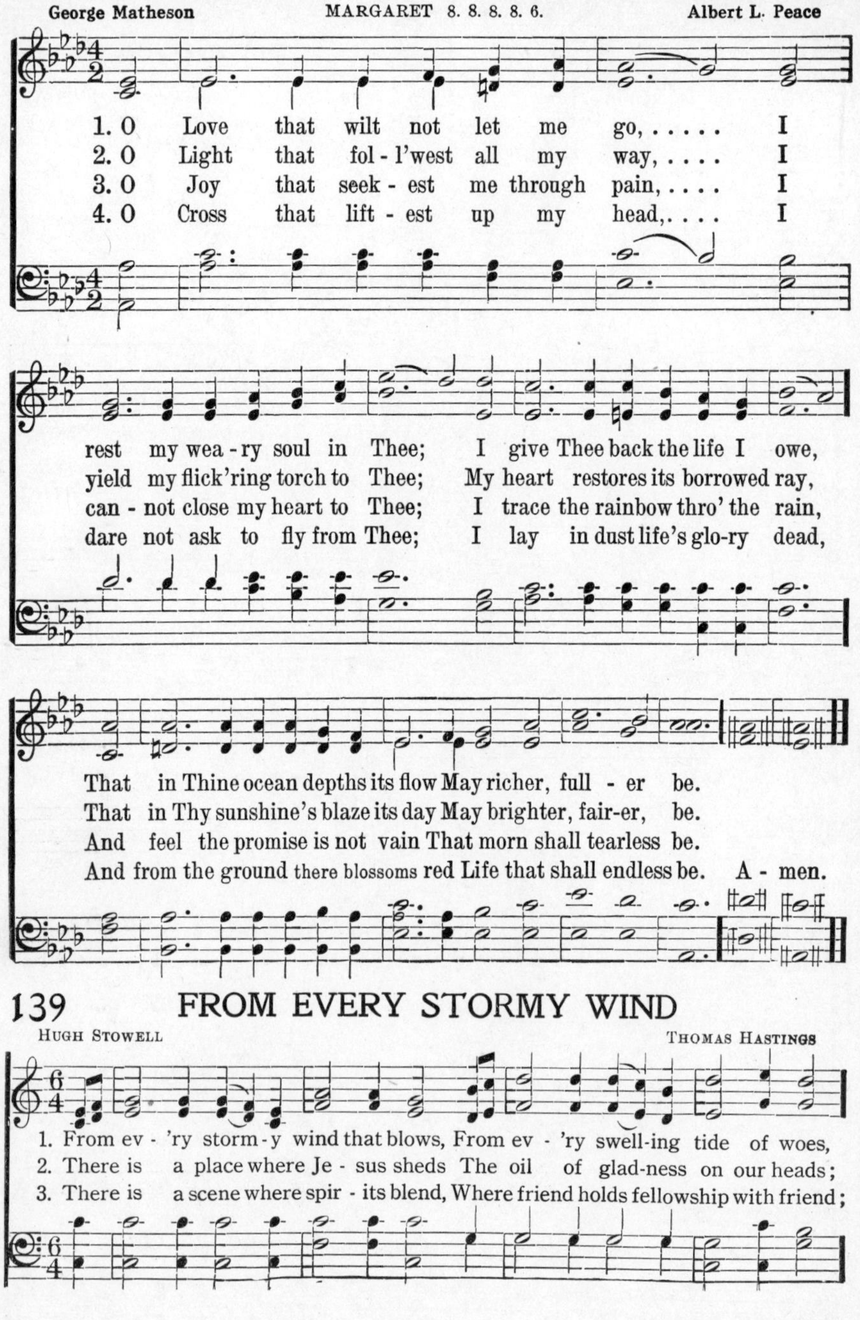
George Matheson
MARGARET 8. 8. 8. 8. 6.
Albert L. Peace
1. O Love that wilt not let me go, ... I rest my wea-ry soul in Thee; I give Thee back the life I owe, That in Thine ocean depths its flow May richer, full - er be.
2. O Light that fol-l'west all my way, ... I yield my flick'ring torch to Thee; My heart restores its borrowed ray, That in Thy sunshine's blaze its day May brighter, fair-er, be.
3. O Joy that seek-est me through pain, ... I can-not close my heart to Thee; I trace the rainbow thro' the rain, And feel the promise is not vain That morn shall tearless be.
4. O Cross that lift-est up my head, ... I dare not ask to fly from Thee; I lay in dust life's glo-ry dead, And from the ground there blossoms red Life that shall endless be. A - men.
139 FROM EVERY STORMY WIND
HUGH STOWELL
THOMAS HASTINGS
1. From ev - 'ry storm-y wind that blows, From ev - 'ry swell-ing tide of woes,
2. There is a place where Je - sus sheds The oil of glad-ness on our heads;
3. There is a scene where spir - its blend, Where friend holds fellowship with friend;

FROM EVERY STORMY WIND
There is a calm, a sure re-treat: 'Tis found be - neath the mer - cy - seat.
A place than all be - sides more sweet: It is the blood-bought mer - cy - seat.
Tho' sun-dered far, by faith they meet A-round the com-mon mer - cy - seat.
140 LET THE LOWER LIGHTS BE BURNING
P. P. B.
Used by permission
P. P. Bliss
1. Bright-ly beams our Fa-ther's mer-cy From His lighthouse ev - er - more;
2. Dark the night of sin has set-tled, Loud the an - gry bil-lows roar;
3. Trim your fee - ble lamp, my brother! Some poor sea - man, tempest-tossed,
But to us He gives the keep-ing Of the lights a - long the shore.
Ea - ger eyes are watching, long-ing, For the lights a - long the shore.
Try - ing now to make the har-bor, In the dark-ness may be lost.
Chorus
Let the low - er lights be burning! Send a gleam a-cross the wave!
Some poor fainting, struggling sea-man You may res - cue, you may save.

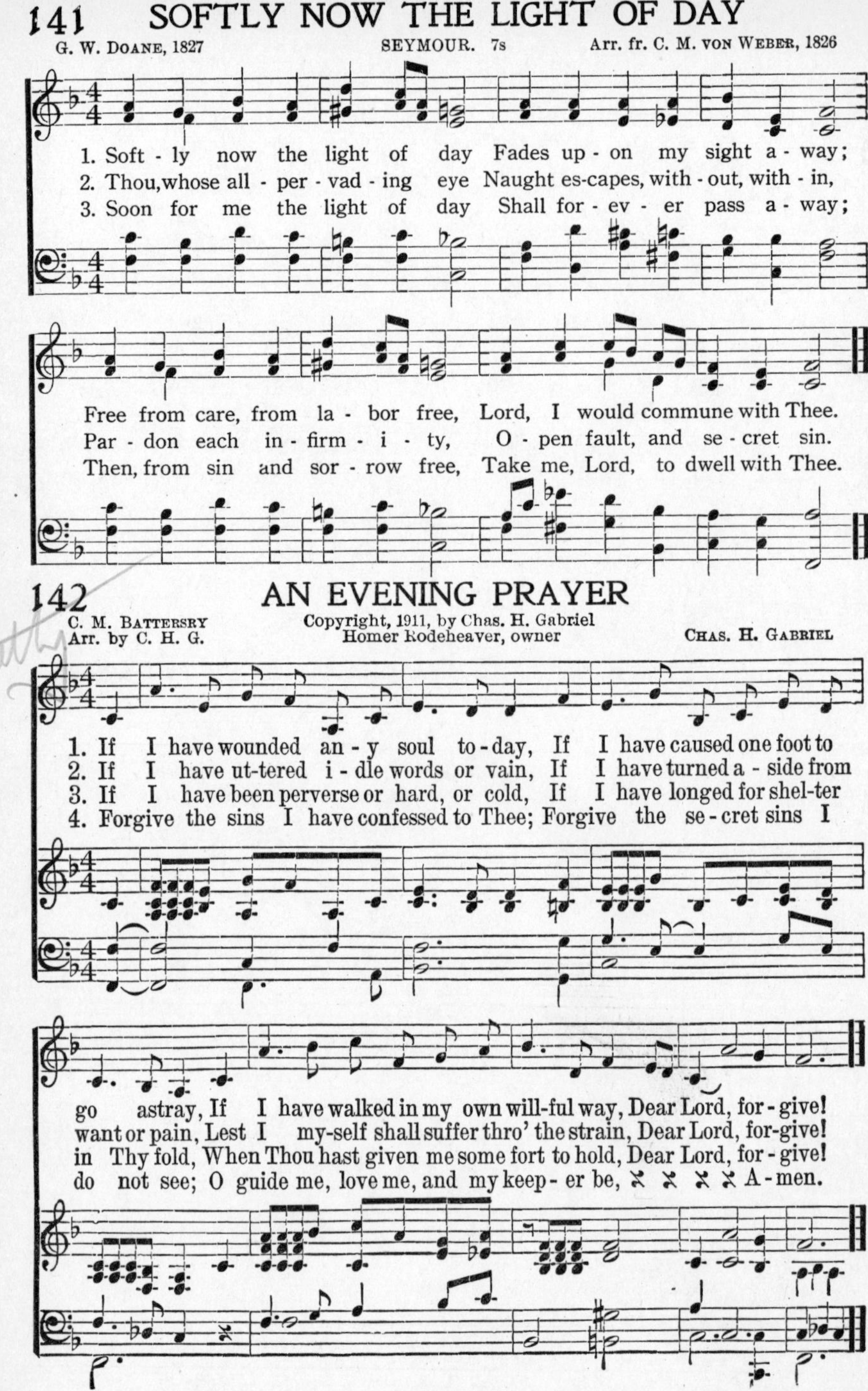
141 SOFTLY NOW THE LIGHT OF DAY
G. W. Doane, 1827
SEYMOUR. 7s
Arr. fr. C. M. von Weber, 1826
1. Soft - ly now the light of day Fades up - on my sight a - way;
2. Thou, whose all - per - vad - ing eye Naught es-capes, with - out, with - in,
3. Soon for me the light of day Shall for - ev - er pass a - way;
Free from care, from la - bor free, Lord, I would commune with Thee.
Par - don each in - firm - i - ty, O - pen fault, and se - cret sin.
Then, from sin and sor - row free, Take me, Lord, to dwell with Thee.
142 AN EVENING PRAYER
C. M. Battersby
Arr. by C. H. G.
Copyright, 1911, by Chas. H. Gabriel
Homer Rodeheaver, owner
Chas. H. Gabriel
1. If I have wounded an - y soul to - day, If I have caused one foot to
2. If I have ut-tered i - dle words or vain, If I have turned a - side from
3. If I have been perverse or hard, or cold, If I have longed for shel-ter
4. Forgive the sins I have confessed to Thee; Forgive the se - cret sins I
go astray, If I have walked in my own will-ful way, Dear Lord, for - give!
want or pain, Lest I my-self shall suffer thro' the strain, Dear Lord, for-give!
in Thy fold, When Thou hast given me some fort to hold, Dear Lord, for - give!
do not see; O guide me, love me, and my keep - er be, A - men.

143 O FOR A THOUSAND TONGUES

AZMON

Charles Wesley

Carl G. Glaser
Arr. by Lowell Mason

1. O for a thou-sand tongues to sing My great Re-deem-er's praise,
The glo-ries of my God and King, The triumphs of His grace.

2. My gracious Mas-ter and my God, As-sist me to pro-claim,
To spread thro' all the earth a-broad The hon-ors of Thy name.

3. Je-sus! the name that charms our fears, That bids our sor-rows cease;
'Tis mu-sic in the sin-ner's ears, 'Tis life, and health, and peace.

4. He breaks the pow'r of canceled sin, He sets the pris-'ner free;
His blood can make the foul-est clean; His blood a-vailed for me.

5. Hear Him, ye deaf; His praise, ye dumb, Your loosened tongues em-ploy;
Ye blind, be-hold your Sav-ior come; And leap, ye lame, for joy.

144 O GOD, OUR HELP IN AGES PAST

Isaac Watts

ST. ANNE C. M.

William Croft

1. O God, our help in a-ges past, Our hope for years to come,
Our shel-ter from the storm-y blast, And our e-ter-nal home!  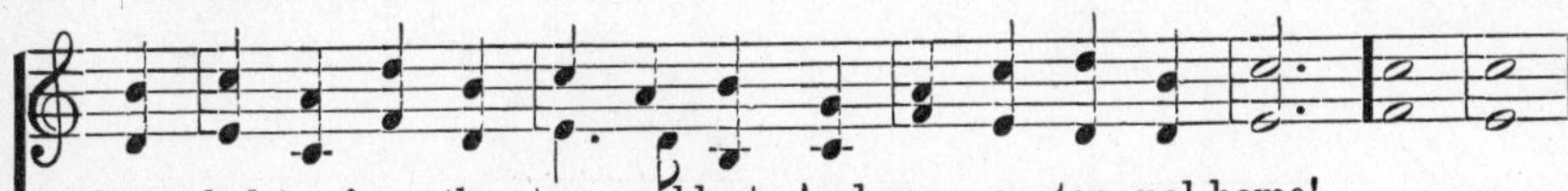

2. Be-fore the hills in or-der stood, Or earth re-ceived her frame,
From ev-er-last-ing Thou art God, To end-less years the same.

3. A thous-and a-ges, in Thy sight, Are like an ev-'ning gone;
Short as the watch that ends the night, Be-fore the ris-ing sun.

4. Time, like an ev-er-roll-ing stream, Bears all its sons a-way;
They fly, for-got-ten, as a dream Dies at the ope-ning day.

5. O God, our help in a-ges past, Our hope for years to come;
Be Thou our guide while life shall last, And our e-ter-nal home! A-men.

YOU CAN SMILE

A. H. A. — A. H. Ackley

1. There are many troubles that will burst like bubbles, There are many shadows that will disappear, When you learn to meet them, with a smile to greet them, For a smile is better than a frown or tear.
2. Tho' the world forsake you, joy will overtake you, Hope will soon awake you, if you smile to-day; Don't parade your sorrow, wait until to-morrow, For your joy aud hope will drive the clouds away.
3. When the clouds are raining, don't begin complaining, What the earth is gaining should not make you sad; Do not be a fretter, smiling is much better, And a smile will help to make the whole world glad.

CHORUS.

You can smile when you can't say a word, You can smile when you cannot be heard, You can smile . . . when its cloudy or fair, You can smile any time, a-ny-where.

8va

FACE TO FACE

Mrs. Frank A. Breck — Grant Colfax Tullar

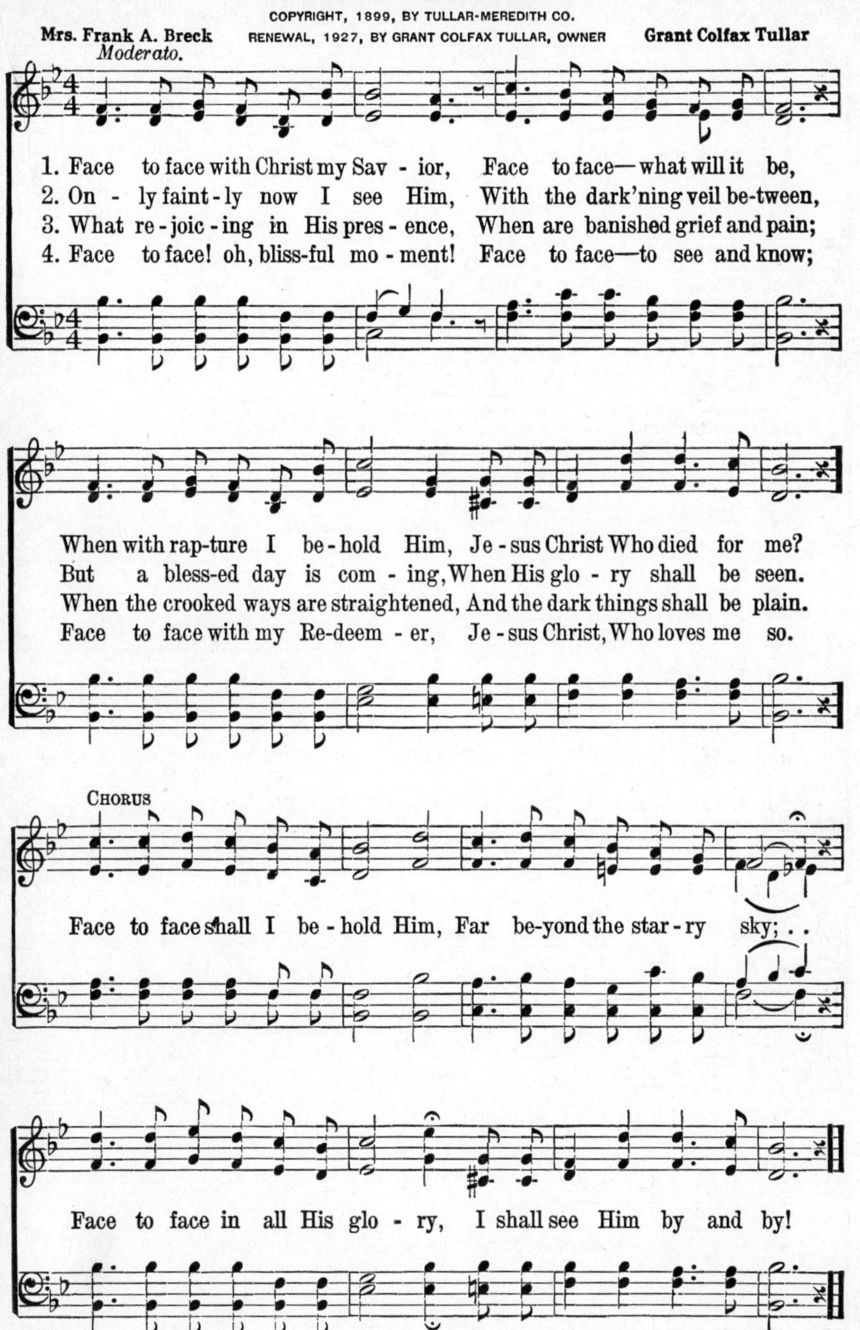
Moderato.
1. Face to face with Christ my Sav - ior, Face to face—what will it be,
2. On - ly faint-ly now I see Him, With the dark'ning veil be-tween,
3. What re-joic-ing in His pres-ence, When are banished grief and pain;
4. Face to face! oh, bliss-ful mo - ment! Face to face—to see and know;
When with rap-ture I be-hold Him, Je-sus Christ Who died for me?
But a bless-ed day is com - ing, When His glo - ry shall be seen.
When the crooked ways are straightened, And the dark things shall be plain.
Face to face with my Re-deem - er, Je-sus Christ, Who loves me so.
CHORUS
Face to face shall I be-hold Him, Far be-yond the star-ry sky; . .
Face to face in all His glo - ry, I shall see Him by and by!

147 WHITER THAN SNOW

James Nicholson — William G. Fischer

1. Lord Je - sus, I long to be per - fect - ly whole; I want Thee for - ev - er, to live in my soul; Break down ev - 'ry i - dol, cast out ev - 'ry foe; Now wash me, and I shall be whit - er than snow.
2. Lord Je - sus, look down from Thy throne in the skies, And help me to make a com - plete sac - ri - fice; I give up my - self, and what - ev - er I know: Now wash me, and I shall be whit - er than snow.
3. Lord Je - sus, for this I most hum - bly en - treat; I wait, bless - ed Lord, at Thy cru - ci - fied feet, By faith, for my cleansing I see Thy blood flow: Now wash me, and I shall be whit - er than snow.
4. Lord Je - sus, Thou seest I pa - tient - ly wait; Come now, and with - in me a new heart cre - ate; To those who have sought Thee, Thou nev - er said'st No: Now wash me, and I shall be whit - er than snow.
CHORUS
Whit - er than snow, yes, whit - er than snow;
Now wash me, and I shall be whit - er than snow.

148 THE OLD-TIME RELIGION

"The hope set before us: which we have as an anchor of the soul, both sure and steadfast, and entereth into that within the veil."—HEB. 6: 18, 19

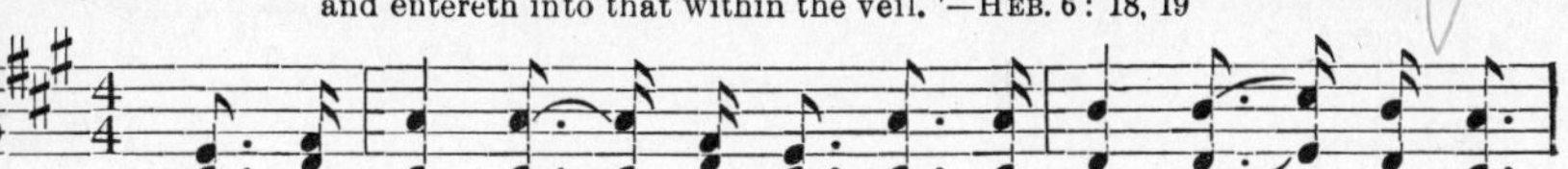

CHORUS—'Tis the old-time re-lig-ion, 'Tis the old-time re-lig-ion,
1. It was good for our mothers, It was good for our mothers,
2. Makes me love ev-'ry-bod-y, Makes me love ev-'ry-bod-y,
3. It has saved our fa-thers, It has saved our fa-thers,

'Tis the old-time re-lig-ion, And it's good e-nough for me!
It was good for our moth-ers, And it's good e-nough for me!
Makes me love ev-'ry-bod-y, And it's good e-nough for me!
It has saved our fa-thers, And it's good e-nough for me!

4 ‖: Makes me love the good old Bible, :‖
And it's good enough for me!

5 ‖: It will lead me to Jesus, :‖
And it's good enough for me!

6 ‖: It will do when I am dying, :‖
And it's good enough for me!

7 ‖: It will take us all to heaven, :‖
And it's good enough for me!

149 THE SACRED BOOK

THOMAS KELLY — HAMBURG. L. M. — Gregorian

1. I love the sa-cred Book of God, No oth-er can its place sup-ply;
2. Sweet Book! in thee my eyes dis-cern The im-age of my ab-sent Lord;
3. But, while I'm here, thou shalt sup-ply His place, and tell me of His love;

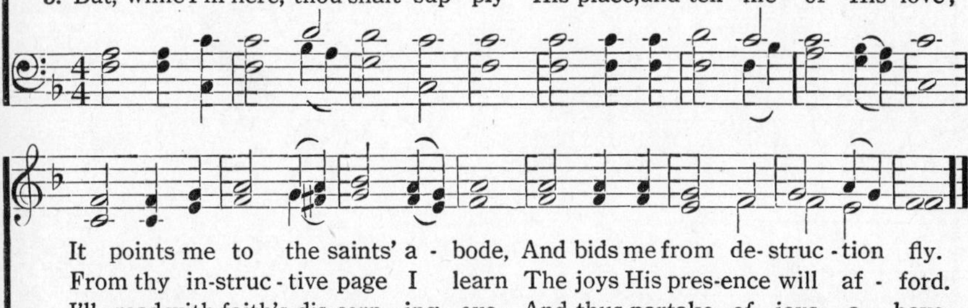

It points me to the saints' a-bode, And bids me from de-struc-tion fly.
From thy in-struc-tive page I learn The joys His pres-ence will af-ford.
I'll read with faith's dis-cern-ing eye, And thus partake of joys a-bove.

150 I WILL SING THE WONDROUS STORY

F. H. ROWLEY — PETER P. BILHORN

1. I will sing the won-drous sto - ry Of the Christ who died for me,
2. I was lost, but Je - sus found me, Found the sheep that went a - stray,
3. I was bruised, but Je - sus healed me; Faint was I from man-y a fall;
4. Days of dark-ness still come o'er me, Sor-row's paths I oft - en tread,
5. He will keep me till the riv - er Rolls its wa - ters at my feet;
How He left His home in glo - ry For the cross of Cal - va - ry.
Threw His lov - ing arms a - round me, Drew me back in - to His way.
Sight was gone, and fears pos-sessed me, But He freed me from them all.
But the Sav - iour still is with me; By His hand I'm safe - ly led.
Then He'll bear me safe - ly o - ver, Where the loved ones I shall meet.
CHORUS
Yes, I'll sing . . . . . the won-drous sto - ry Of the
Yes, I'll sing
the won-drous sto - ry
Christ . . . . who died for me, ... Sing it with . . . . .the saints in
Of the Christ
who died for me,
Sing it with
glo - ry, Gath-ered by . . . . . . the crys-tal sea . . . .
the saints in glo - ry,
Gath-ered by
the crystal sea.

151 O MASTER, LET ME WALK WITH THEE

WASHINGTON GLADDEN — H. PERCY SMITH

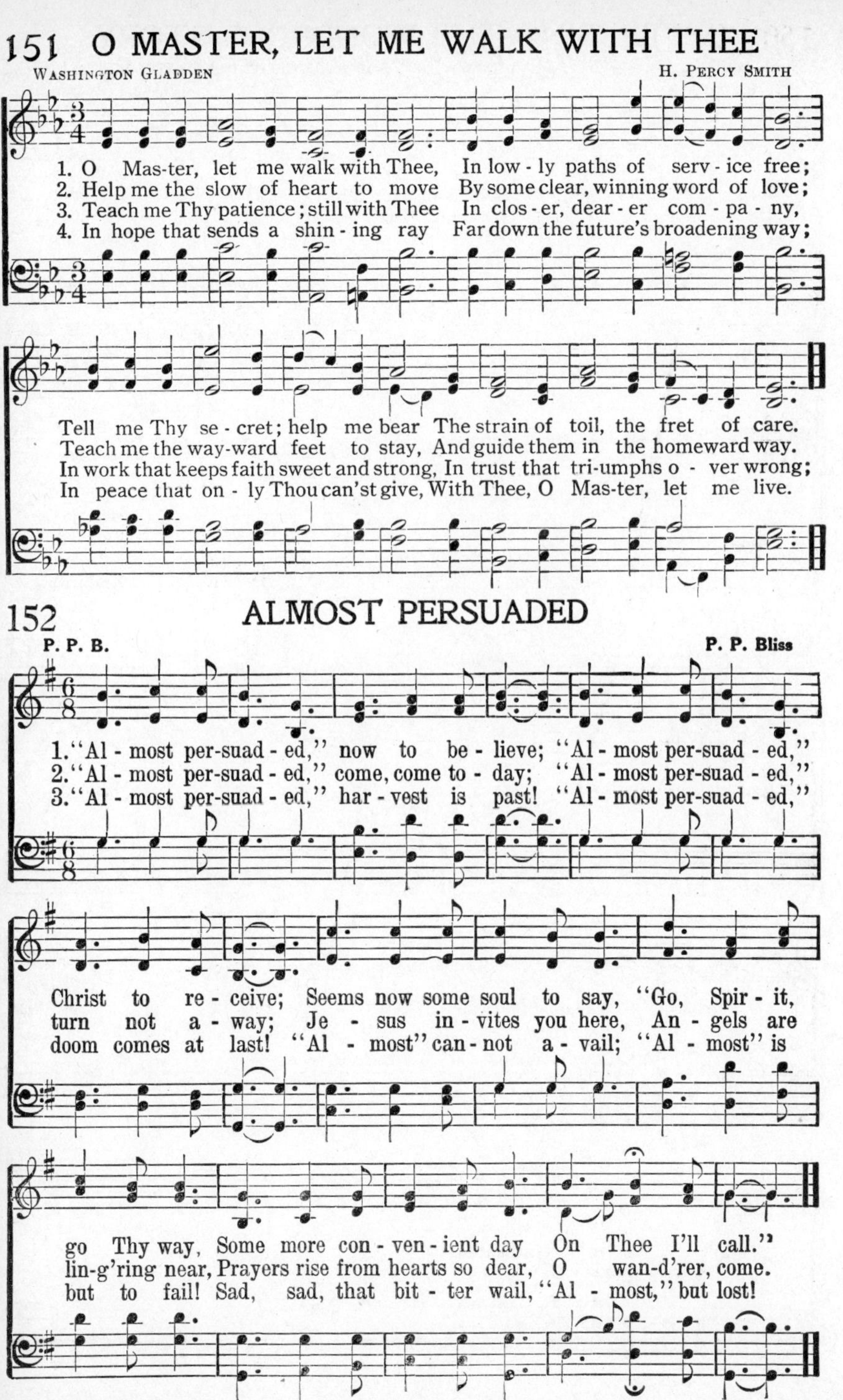
1. O Mas-ter, let me walk with Thee, In low - ly paths of serv - ice free; Tell me Thy se - cret; help me bear The strain of toil, the fret of care.
2. Help me the slow of heart to move By some clear, winning word of love; Teach me the way-ward feet to stay, And guide them in the homeward way.
3. Teach me Thy patience; still with Thee In clos - er, dear - er com - pa - ny, In work that keeps faith sweet and strong, In trust that tri-umphs o - ver wrong;
4. In hope that sends a shin - ing ray Far down the future's broadening way; In peace that on - ly Thou can'st give, With Thee, O Mas-ter, let me live.

152 ALMOST PERSUADED

P. P. B. — P. P. Bliss

1. "Al - most per-suad - ed," now to be - lieve; "Al - most per-suad - ed," Christ to re - ceive; Seems now some soul to say, "Go, Spir - it, go Thy way, Some more con - ven - ient day On Thee I'll call."
2. "Al - most per-suad - ed," come, come to - day; "Al - most per-suad - ed," turn not a - way; Je - sus in - vites you here, An - gels are lin-g'ring near, Prayers rise from hearts so dear, O wan-d'rer, come.
3. "Al - most per-suad - ed," har - vest is past! "Al - most per-suad - ed," doom comes at last! "Al - most" can - not a - vail; "Al - most" is but to fail! Sad, sad, that bit - ter wail, "Al - most," but lost!

153 BRING THEM IN

ALEXCENAH THOMAS — Property of Mrs. W. A. Ogden — W. A. OGDEN

1. Hark! 'tis the Shepherd's voice I hear, Out in the des - ert dark and drear, Call - ing the sheep who've gone a - stray, Far from the Shep-herd's fold a - way.
2. Who'll go and help this Shep - herd kind, Help Him the wan-d'ring ones to find? Who'll bring the lost ones to the fold, Where they'll be shel - tered from the cold?
3. Out in the des - ert hear their cry, Out on the moun-tains wild and high; Hark! 'tis the Mas - ter speaks to thee, "Go, find My sheep wher - e'er they be."
CHORUS
Bring them in, bring them in, Bring them in from the fields of sin; Bring them in, bring them in, Bring the wand'ring ones to Je - sus.

SAFELY THROUGH ANOTHER WEEK

JOHN NEWTON LOWELL MASON

1. Safe - ly through an - oth - er week God has brought us on our way;
2. While we pray for par-d'ning grace, Thro' the dear Re-deem-er's name,
3. Here we come Thy name to praise, Let us feel Thy pres-ence near;
4. May Thy gos-pel's joy - ful sound Con - quer sin - ners, com-fort saints;
Let us now a bless - ing seek, Wait - ing in His courts to - day;
Show Thy rec - on - cil - ed face; Take a - way our sin and shame:
May Thy glo - ry meet our eyes, While we in Thy house ap - pear:
Make the fruits of grace a - bound, Bring re - lief for all com - plaints:
Day of all the week the best, Em-blem of e - ter - nal rest: Day of
From our world-ly cares set free, May we rest this day in Thee: From our
Here af - ford us, Lord, a taste Of our ev - er-last - ing feast: Here af-
Thus may all our Sab-baths prove, Till we join the Church a - bove: Thus may
all the week the best, Em - blem of e - ter - nal rest.
world-ly cares set free, May we rest this day in Thee.
ford us, Lord, a taste Of our ev - er - last - ing feast.
all our Sab-baths prove, Till we join the Church a - bove. A - MEN.

155 ONE SWEETLY SOLEMN THOUGHT

"Now they desire a better country, that is, an heavenly."—HEB. 11 : 16

PHOEBE CARY | PHILIP PHILLIPS

1. One sweet-ly sol-emn tho't Comes to me o'er and o'er; I'm near-er home to-day, to-day, Than I have been be-fore.
2. Near-er my Father's house, Where many mansions be; Near-er the great white throne to-day, Near-er the crys-tal sea.
3. Near-er the bound of life, Where burdens are laid down; Nearer to leave the cross to-day, And nearer to the crown.
4. Be near me when my feet Are slip-ping o'er the brink; For I am near-er home to-day, Per-haps, than now I think.
CHORUS
Near-er my home, Nearer my home, Near-er my home to-day, to-day, Than I have been be-fore.
156 FIGHT THE GOOD FIGHT
"Fight the good fight of faith, lay hold on eternal life."—1 TIM. 6 : 12
J. S. B. MONSELL
PENTECOST. L. M.
W. BOYD
1. Fight the good fight with all thy might, Christ is thy strength, and Christ thy right;
2. Run the straight race thro' God's good grace, Lift up thine eyes, and seek His face;
3. Cast care a-side, lean on thy Guide; His boundless mer-cy will pro-vide;
4. Faint not, nor fear, His arms are near; He changeth not, and thou art dear;

FIGHT THE GOOD FIGHT

Lay hold on life, and it shall be Thy joy and crown e - ter - nal - ly.
Life with its way be- fore thee lies, Christ is the path, and Christ the prize.
Trust, and thy trusting soul shall prove Christ is its life, and Christ its love.
On - ly be- lieve, and thou shalt see That Christ is all and all to thee.

157 MY HEAVENLY HOME

WILLIAM HUNTER — Arr. WILLIAM McDONALD

1. My heav'nly home is bright and fair; Nor pain, nor death can en - ter there;
Its glitt'ring tow'rs the sun out-shine; That heav'nly man - sion shall be mine.

2. My Father's house is built on high, Far, far a - bove the star - ry sky;
When from this earth - ly pris - on free, That heav'nly man - sion mine shall be.

3. While here, a stran - ger far from home, Af-fliction's waves may round me foam;
Al-though, like Laz - arus, sick and poor, My heav'nly man - sion is se - cure.

4. Let oth - ers seek a home be - low, Which flames devour, or waves o'er-flow;
Be mine the hap - pier lot to own A heav'nly man - sion near the throne.

CHORUS

I'm go - ing home, I'm go - ing home, I'm go - ing home to die no more,
To die no more, To die no more, I'm go - ing home to die no more.

158 BLESSED HOUR OF PRAYER

FANNY J. CROSBY — W. H. DOANE

1. 'Tis the blessed hour of prayer, when our hearts lowly bend, And we gath - er to
2. 'Tis the blessed hour of prayer, when the Savior draws near, With a ten-der com-
3. 'Tis the blessed hour of prayer, when the tempted and tried To the Sav - ior who
4. At the blessed hour of prayer, trusting Him we be-lieve That the blessings we're
Je - sus, our Savior and Friend; If we come to Him in faith, His pro-tection to share,
pas - sion His childrento hear; When He tells us we may cast at His feet ev'ry care,
loves them their sorrows confide; With a sympathizing heart He removes ev'ry care;
need-ing we'll sure-ly re-ceive, In the fulness of this trust we shall lose ev'ry care;
What a balm for the wea-ry! O how sweet to be there!
CHORUS
Blessed hour of prayer,
Blessed hour of prayer, What a balm for the wea-ry! O how sweet to be there!

159 BEHOLD A STRANGER

REV. J. GRIGG — "Behold, I stand at the door, and knock."—REV. 3: 20 — HENRY K. OLIVER

1. Be - hold a Stran - ger at the door, He gen-tly knocks, has knock'd before;
2. O love-ly at - . ti - tude! He stands With melting heart and la - den hands;
3. But will He prove a Friend in - deed? He will, the ver - y Friend you need;
4. Rise, touch'd with grati - tude di - vine; Turn out His en - e - my and thine,

BEHOLD A STRANGER

160 I AM SO GLAD THAT OUR FATHER IN HEAVEN

P. P. B. JESUS LOVES ME P. P. Bliss

Has wait-ed long,—is wait - ing still; You treat no oth - er friend so ill.
O matchless kindness! and He shows This matchless kindness to His foes.
The Friend of sin - ners, yes, 'tis He, With garments dyed on Cal - va - ry.
That soul-de-stroy - ing mons - ter, Sin; And let the heavenly Stran-ger in.
1. I am so glad that our Father in heav'n Tells of His love in the Book He has giv'n;
2. Tho' I for - get Him and wander away, Kind-ly He follows wherev - er I stray;
3. Oh, if there's on-ly one song I can sing, When in His beauty I see the great King,
Won-der-ful things in the Bi - ble I see, This is the dearest, that Jesus loves me.
Back to His dear lov-ing arms would I flee, When I re-member that Jesus loves me.
This shall my song in e - ter - ni - ty be, Oh, what a wonder that Jesus loves me!
Refrain
I am so glad that Je-sus loves me, Je - sus loves me, Je - sus loves me;
I am so glad that Je - sus loves me, Je - sus loves e - ven me.

161 TELL MOTHER I'LL BE THERE

C. M. F. CHARLES M. FILLMORE

1. When I was but a lit-tle child how well I rec-ol-lect How I would grieve my moth-er with my fol-ly and neg-lect;
2. Though I was oft-en wayward, she was al-ways kind and good; So pa-tient, gen-tle, lov-ing, when I act-ed rough and rude;
3. When I be-came a prod-i-gal, and left the old roof-tree, She al-most broke her lov-ing heart in mourn-ing aft-er me;
4. One day a mes-sage came to me, it bade me quick-ly come If I would see my moth-er ere the Sav-ior took her home;
And now that she has gone to heav'n I miss her ten-der care:
My child-hood griefs and tri-als she would glad-ly with me share:
And day and night she prayed to God to keep me in His care:
I prom-ised her, be-fore she died, for heav-en to pre-pare;
O Sav-ior, tell my moth-er, I'll be there!
CHORUS
Tell moth-er I'll be there in an-swer to her pray'r, This

TELL MOTHER I'LL BE THERE

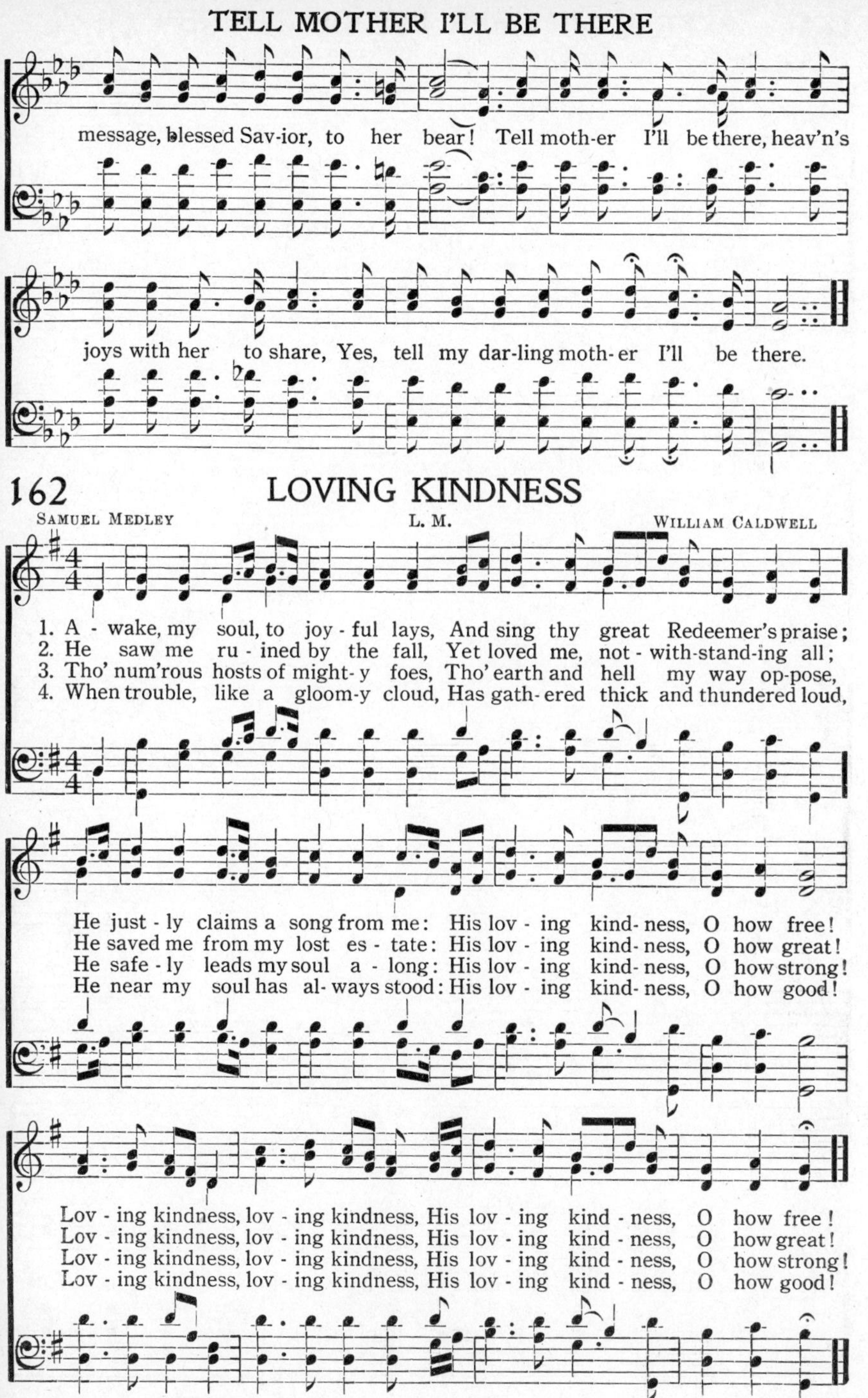
message, blessed Sav-ior, to her bear! Tell moth-er I'll be there, heav'n's
joys with her to share, Yes, tell my dar-ling moth- er I'll be there.
162
LOVING KINDNESS
SAMUEL MEDLEY
L. M.
WILLIAM CALDWELL
1. A - wake, my soul, to joy - ful lays, And sing thy great Redeemer's praise;
2. He saw me ru - ined by the fall, Yet loved me, not - with-stand-ing all;
3. Tho' num'rous hosts of might- y foes, Tho' earth and hell my way op-pose,
4. When trouble, like a gloom-y cloud, Has gath- ered thick and thundered loud,
He just - ly claims a song from me: His lov - ing kind- ness, O how free!
He saved me from my lost es - tate: His lov - ing kind- ness, O how great!
He safe - ly leads my soul a - long: His lov - ing kind- ness, O how strong!
He near my soul has al- ways stood: His lov - ing kind- ness, O how good!
Lov - ing kindness, lov - ing kindness, His lov - ing kind - ness, O how free!
Lov - ing kindness, lov - ing kindness, His lov - ing kind - ness, O how great!
Lov - ing kindness, lov - ing kindness, His lov - ing kind - ness, O how strong!
Lov - ing kindness, lov - ing kindness, His lov - ing kind - ness, O how good!

163 PULL FOR THE SHORE

"Therefore, if any man be in Christ, he is a new creature; old things are passed away, behold, all things are become new."—2 Cor. 5 : 17

"Therefore, my beloved, * * * work out your own salvation with fear and trembling."—Phil. 2 : 12

P. P. B. P. P. Bliss. By per.

1. Light in the darkness, sailor, day is at hand! See o'er the foaming billows fair Haven's land. Drear was the voy-age, sail-or, now al-most o'er, Safe with-in the life-boat, sail-or, pull for the shore.

2. Trust in the life-boat, sailor, all else will fail, Stron-ger the sur-ges dash and fierc-er the gale; Heed not the storm-y winds, tho' loud-ly they roar; Watch the "bright and morn-ing star," and pull for the shore.

3. Bright gleams the morning, sailor, up lift the eye; Clouds and darkness disappearing, glo-ry is nigh! Safe in the life-boat, sail-or, sing ev-er-more; "Glo-ry, glo-ry, hal-le-lu-jah!" pull for the shore.

Chorus

Pull for the shore, sail-or, pull for the shore! Heed not the roll-ing waves, but

PULL FOR THE SHORE
bend to the oar. Safe in the life-boat, sail - or, cling to self no more!
Leave the poor old strand - ed wreck, and pull for the shore.
164 EVEN ME, EVEN ME
Mrs. Elizabeth Codner
William B. Bradbury
1. Lord, I hear of show'rs of bless- ing Thou art scat-t'ring full and free;
2. Pass me not, O God, my Fa - ther, Sin - ful tho' my heart may be;
3. Pass me not, O gra- cious Sav - ior, Let me live and cling to Thee;
4. Love of God, so pure and changeless, Blood of Christ, so rich and free;
Show'rs, the thirst - y land re- fresh - ing; Let some drops now fall on me;
Thou mightst leave me, but the rath - er, Let Thy mer - cy light on me;
I am long - ing for Thy fa - vor; Whilst Thou'rt calling, oh! call me;
Grace of God, so strong and boundless, Mag - ni - fy them all in me;
E - ven me, e - ven me, Let some drops now fall on me.
E - ven me, e - ven me, Let Thy mer - cy light on me.
E - ven me, e - ven me, Whilst Thou'rt call - ing, oh! call me.
E - ven me, e - ven me, Mag - ni - fy them all in me.

165 PASS ME NOT

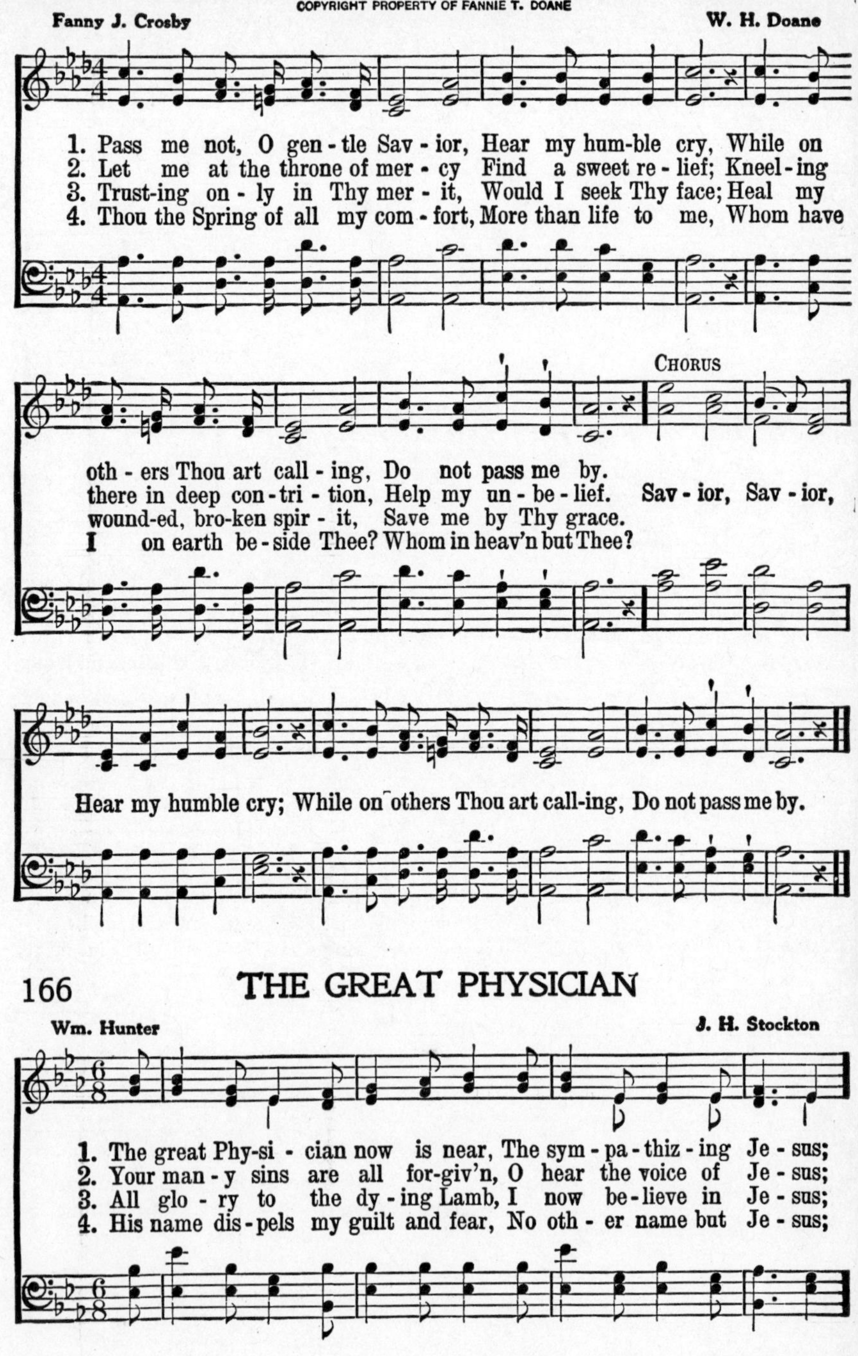
COPYRIGHT PROPERTY OF FANNIE T. DOANE
Fanny J. Crosby
W. H. Doane
1. Pass me not, O gen-tle Sav-ior, Hear my hum-ble cry, While on oth-ers Thou art call-ing, Do not pass me by.
2. Let me at the throne of mer-cy Find a sweet re-lief; Kneel-ing there in deep con-tri-tion, Help my un-be-lief.
3. Trust-ing on-ly in Thy mer-it, Would I seek Thy face; Heal my wound-ed, bro-ken spir-it, Save me by Thy grace.
4. Thou the Spring of all my com-fort, More than life to me, Whom have I on earth be-side Thee? Whom in heav'n but Thee?
CHORUS
Sav-ior, Sav-ior, Hear my humble cry; While on others Thou art call-ing, Do not pass me by.
166
THE GREAT PHYSICIAN
Wm. Hunter
J. H. Stockton
1. The great Phy-si-cian now is near, The sym-pa-thiz-ing Je-sus;
2. Your man-y sins are all for-giv'n, O hear the voice of Je-sus;
3. All glo-ry to the dy-ing Lamb, I now be-lieve in Je-sus;
4. His name dis-pels my guilt and fear, No oth-er name but Je-sus;

THE GREAT PHYSICIAN

FINE.
He speaks the droop-ing heart to cheer, O hear the voice of Je - sus.
Go on your way in peace to heav'n, And wear a crown with Je - sus.
I love the bless-ed Sav-ior's name, I love the name of Je - sus.
Oh! how my soul de-lights to hear The charming name of Je - sus.
D. S.—Sweet-est car - ol ev - er sung, Je - sus, bless-ed Je - sus.
REFRAIN
D. S.
Sweet-est note in ser - aph song, Sweet-est name on mor - tal tongue,

167 COME, THOU FOUNT

ROBERT ROBINSON JOHN WYETH

FINE
1. Come, Thou Fount of ev-'ry bless - ing, Tune my heart to sing Thy grace;
Streams of mer - cy, nev-er ceas - ing, Call for songs of loud-est praise.
2. Here I'll raise my Eb-en - e - zer, Hith-er by Thy help I'll come;
And I hope by Thy good pleasure, Safe-ly to ar - rive at home.
3. Oh, to grace how great a debt - or Dai-ly I'm constrained to be!
Let Thy goodness, like a fet - ter, Bind my wand'ring heart to Thee:
D. C.—Praise the mount, I'm fixed up - on it! Mount of Thy re - deem-ing love.
D. C.—He, to res - cue me from dan - ger, In - ter-posed His pre-cious blood.
D. C.—Here's my heart, O take and seal it, Seal it for Thy courts a - bove.
D. C.
Teach me some mel - o-dious son-net, Sung by flam-ing tongues a-bove;
Je - sus sought me when a stranger, Wand'ring from the fold of God;
Prone to love Thee, Lord, I feel it, Prone to serve the God I love;

168 I NEED THEE EVERY HOUR

MRS. ANNIE S. HAWKS
REV. ROBERT LOWRY
1. I need Thee ev - 'ry hour, Most gra-cious Lord; No ten - der voice like
2. I need Thee ev - 'ry hour, Stay Thou near by; Temp-ta - tions lose their
3. I need Thee ev - 'ry hour, In joy or pain; Come quick-ly and a -
4. I need Thee ev - 'ry hour, Most Ho - ly One; O make me Thine in -
CHORUS
Thine Can peace af - ford.
pow'r When Thou art nigh. I need Thee, O I need Thee; Ev - 'ry hour I
bide, Or life is vain.
deed, Thou bless-ed Son!
need Thee! O bless me now, my Sav - ior, I come to Thee!
169 WHERE CROSS THE CROWDED WAYS OF LIFE
F. MASON NORTH
BEETHOVEN
1. Where cross the crowded ways of life, Where sounds the cries of race and clan,
2. In haunts of wretch-ed - ness and need, On shadowed thresholds dark with fears,
3. The cup of wa - ter giv'n for Thee Still holds the freshness of Thy grace;
4. O Mas-ter, from the mountain side, Make haste to heal these hearts of pain,
5. Till sons of men shall learn Thy love And fol-low where Thy feet have trod:

WHERE CROSS THE CROWDED WAYS OF LIFE

A - bove the noise of self-ish strife, We hear Thy voice, O Son of man!
From paths where hide the lures of greed, We catch the vi - sion of Thy tears.
Yet long these mul - ti - tudes to see The sweet com-pas-sion of Thy face.
A - mong these restless throngs a-bide, O tread the cit - y's streets a - gain.
Till glo - rious from Thy heav'n above Shall come the cit - y of our God.

170 O WORSHIP THE KING
Sir Robert Grant
Francis Joseph Haydn
1. O wor - ship the King all - glo - rious a - bove, And grate-ful - ly
2. O tell of His might, and sing of His grace, Whose robe is the
3. Thy boun - ti - ful care what tongue can re - cite? It breathes in the
4. Frail chil-dren of dust, and fee - ble as frail, In Thee do we
sing His won-der - ful love; Our Shield and De - fend-er, the An-cient of
light, whose can - o - py space; His char - iots of wrath the deep thunder-clouds
air, it shines in the light, It streams from the hills, it de-scends to the
trust, nor find Thee to fail; Thy mer - cies how ten - der! how firm to the
days, Pa - vil - ioned in splen-dor, and gird - ed with praise.
form, And dark is His path on the wings of the storm.
plain, And sweet-ly dis - tills in the dew and the rain.
end! Our Mak - er, De - fend - er, Re - deem - er, and Friend, A - MEN.

171 THE SON OF GOD GOES FORTH TO WAR

R. HEBER — H. S. CUTLER

1. The Son of God goes forth to war, A king-ly crown to gain;
2. That mar-tyr first, whose ea-gle eye Could pierce be-yond the grave;
3. A no-ble band, the cho-sen few On whom the Spir-it came;
His blood-stained banner streams a-far: Who fol-lows in His train?
Who saw his Mas-ter in the sky, And called on Him to save.
Twelve valiant saints, their hopes they knew, And mocked the cross and flame.
Who best can drink His cup of woe, Tri-um-phant o-ver pain,
Like Him, with par-don on his tongue, In midst of mor-tal pain,
They met the ty-rant's brandished steel, The li-on's gor-y main;
Who pa-tient bears His cross be-low:—He fol-lows in His train.
He prayed for them that did the wrong; Who fol-lows in His train?
They bowed their heads the stroke to feel: Who fol-lows in their train?

172 FLING OUT THE BANNER, LET IT FLOAT

GEORGE W. DOANE — JOHN B. CALKIN

1. Fling out the ban-ner, let it float Sky-ward and seaward, high and wide;
2. Fling out the ban-ner, heathen lands Shall see from far the glo-rious sight,
3. Fling out the ban-ner, sin-sick souls That sink and per-ish in the strife,
4. Fling out the ban-ner, let it float Sky-ward and seaward, high and wide,

FLING OUT THE BANNER, LET IT FLOAT

The sun that lights its shin - ing folds, The cross on which the Sav - ior died.
And na-tions, crowding to be born, Bap - tize their spir - its in its light.
Shall touch in faith its ra-diant hem, And spring im-mor - tal in - to life.
Our glo - ry on - ly in the cross; Our on - ly hope, the Cru - ci - fied.
173 COME, THOU ALMIGHTY KING
Anonymous
Felice De Giardini
1. Come, Thou Al - might - y King, Help us Thy name to sing,
2. Come, Thou In - car - nate Word, Gird on Thy might - y sword,
3. Come, Ho - ly Com - fort - er, Thy sa - cred wit - ness bear
4. To the great One in Three E - ter - nal prais - es be
Help us to praise: Fa - ther, all - glo - ri - ous, O'er all vic -
Our pray'r at - tend: Come, and Thy peo - ple bless, And give Thy
In this glad hour: Thou who al - might - y art, Now rule in
Hence ev - er - more. His sov-'reign maj - es - ty May we in
to - ri - ous, Come, and reign o - ver us, An - cient of Days.
word suc - cess: Spir - it of ho - li - ness, On us de - scend.
ev - 'ry heart, And ne'er from us de - part, Spir - it of pow'r.
glo - ry see, And to e - ter - ni - ty, Love and a - dore.

174
FAIREST LORD JESUS
Crusaders' Hymn
Arr. by Richard S. Willis
1. Fair - est Lord Je - sus! Rul - er of all na - ture!
2. Fair are the mead - ows, Fair - er still the wood - lands,
3. Fair is the sun - shine, Fair - er still the moon - light,
O Thou of God and man the Son! Thee will I cher - ish,
Robed in the bloom - ing garb of spring; Je - sus is fair - er,
And all the twin - kling star - ry host; Je - sus shines bright - er,
Thee will I hon - or, Thou, my soul's glo - ry, joy, and crown!
Je - sus is pur - er, Who makes the woe - ful heart to sing!
Je - sus shines pur - er, Than all the an - gels heav'n can boast! A - MEN.
175
I LOVE THY KINGDOM, LORD
Timothy Dwight
Aaron Williams
1. I love Thy king - dom, Lord, The house of Thine a - bode, The
2. I love Thy Church, O God! Her walls be - fore Thee stand, Dear
3. For her my tears shall fall; For her my prayers as - cend; To
Church our blest Re - deem - er saved With His own pre - cious blood.
as the ap - ple of Thine eye, And grav - en on Thy hand.
her my cares and toils be giv'n, Till toils and cares shall end. A - MEN.

176 NOW THE DAY IS OVER

SABINE BARING-GOULD Words by permission A. W. Ridley and Co. JOSEPH BARNBY

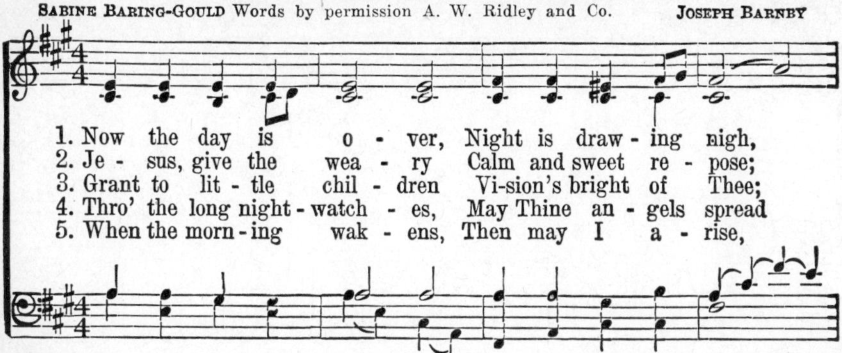

1. Now the day is o - ver, Night is draw - ing nigh,
2. Je - sus, give the wea - ry Calm and sweet re - pose;
3. Grant to lit - tle chil - dren Vi-sion's bright of Thee;
4. Thro' the long night - watch - es, May Thine an - gels spread
5. When the morn - ing wak - ens, Then may I a - rise,

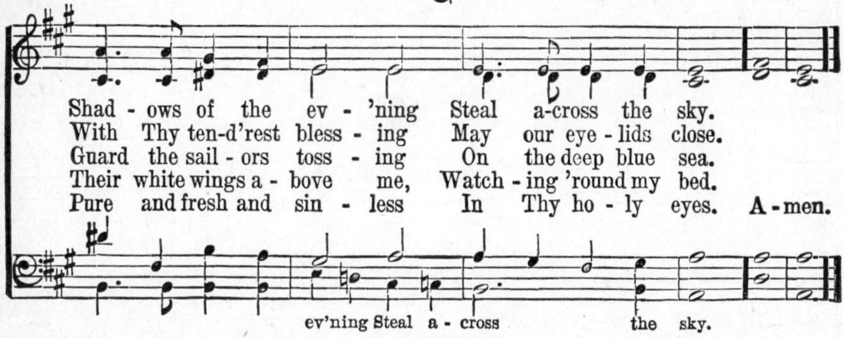

Shad - ows of the ev - 'ning Steal a-cross the sky.
With Thy ten-d'rest bless - ing May our eye - lids close.
Guard the sail - ors toss - ing On the deep blue sea.
Their white wings a - bove me, Watch - ing 'round my bed.
Pure and fresh and sin - less In Thy ho - ly eyes. A - men.

ev'ning Steal a - cross the sky.

177 WHEN I SURVEY THE WONDROUS CROSS

ISAAC WATTS HAMBURG. L. M. Arr. by LOWELL MASON

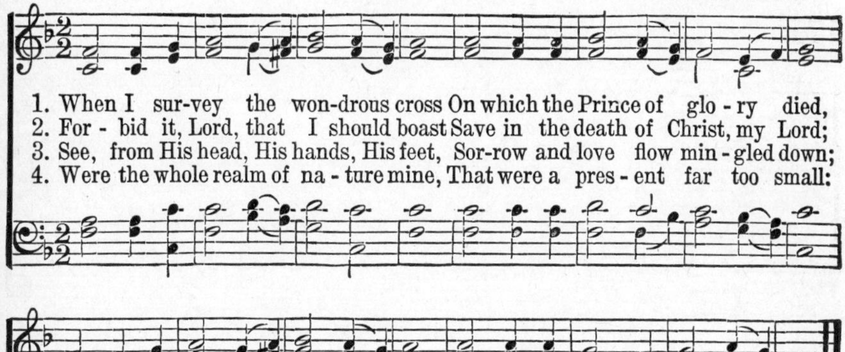

1. When I sur-vey the won-drous cross On which the Prince of glo - ry died,
2. For - bid it, Lord, that I should boast Save in the death of Christ, my Lord;
3. See, from His head, His hands, His feet, Sor-row and love flow min - gled down;
4. Were the whole realm of na - ture mine, That were a pres - ent far too small:

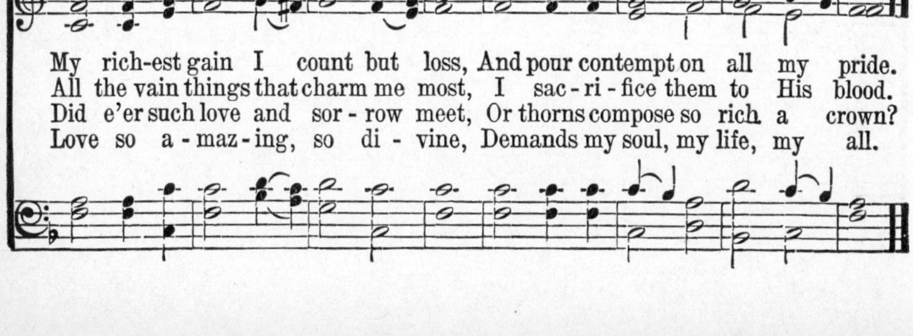

My rich-est gain I count but loss, And pour contempt on all my pride.
All the vain things that charm me most, I sac - ri - fice them to His blood.
Did e'er such love and sor - row meet, Or thorns compose so rich a crown?
Love so a - maz - ing, so di - vine, Demands my soul, my life, my all.

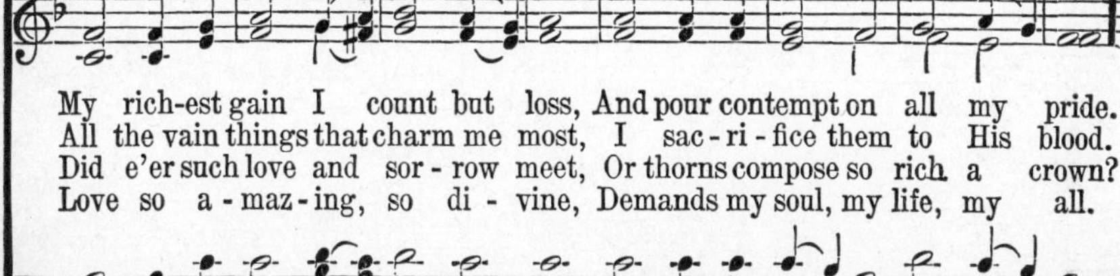

178 I AM THINE, O LORD

FANNY J. CROSBY | W. H. DOANE

1. I am Thine, O Lord, I have heard Thy voice, And it told Thy
2. Con-se-crate me now to Thy serv-ice, Lord, By the pow'r of
3. O the pure de-light of a sin-gle hour That be-fore Thy
4. There are depths of love that I can-not know Till I cross the
love to me; But I long to rise in the arms of faith, And be
grace di-vine; Let my soul look up with a stead-fast hope, And my
throne I spend, When I kneel in prayer, and with Thee, my God, I com-
nar-row sea; There are heights of joy that I may not reach Till I
REFRAIN
clos-er drawn to Thee.
will be lost in Thine. Draw me near - er, near-er, bless-ed
mune as friend with friend!
rest in peace with Thee. near-er, near-er,
Lord, To the cross where Thou hast died; Draw me near-er, near-er,
near-er, bless-ed Lord, To Thy pre-cious, bleed-ing side.

179 ON JORDAN'S STORMY BANKS

Samuel Stennett
Tullius C. O'Kane.
1. On Jor- dan's storm - y banks I stand, And cast a wish - ful eye
2. All o'er those wide - ex - tend - ed plains Shines one e - ter - nal day;
3. No chill - ing winds, nor pois'nous breath, Can reach that health - ful shore;
4. When shall I reach that hap - py place, And be for - ev - er blest?
To Ca- naan's fair and hap - py land, Where my pos - ses - sions lie.
There God the Son for - ev - er reigns, And scat - ters night a - way.
Sick - ness and sor - row, pain and death Are felt and feared no more.
When shall I see my Fa - ther's face, And in His bos - om rest?
Chorus
We will rest in the fair and hap - py land (by and by), Just a -
cross on the ev - er-green shore,............ Sing the song of Mo - ses
ev - er- green shore,
and the Lamb, by and by, And dwell with Je - sus ev - er - more.

180 CROSSING THE BAR

ALFRED TENNYSON | JOSEPH BARNBY

Sun - set and ev - 'ning star, And one clear call for me!
And may there be no moan - ing of the bar, When
I put out to sea, ... But such a tide as
mov - ing seems a - sleep, Too full for sound and foam,
rall.
When that which drew from out the bound - less deep Turns a -

CROSSING THE BAR

gain home . . . Twi - light and ev - 'ning bell, And
Twi - - - light and ev - 'ning bell,
af - ter that the dark! And may there be no sad - ness of fare-well,
cres - - cen - - -
When I em - bark; For, though from out our bourne of time and
- - do rit.
f
place The flood may bear me far, I hope to see my
Pi - lot face to face When I have crossed the bar. A - men,

181 MASTER, THE TEMPEST IS RAGING

MARY A. BAKER

H. R. PALMER

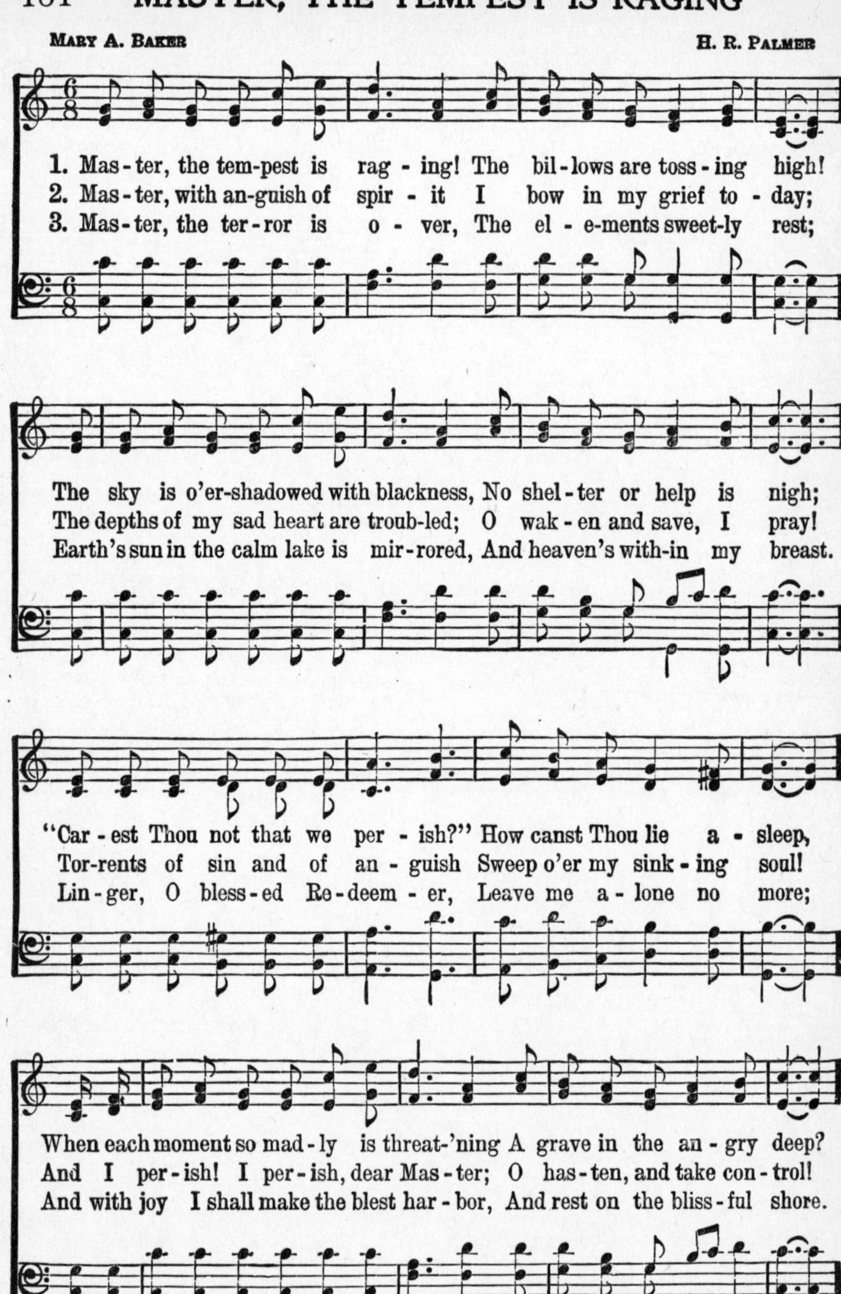
1. Mas-ter, the tem-pest is rag - ing! The bil-lows are toss - ing high!
2. Mas-ter, with an-guish of spir - it I bow in my grief to - day;
3. Mas-ter, the ter-ror is o - ver, The el - e-ments sweet-ly rest;
The sky is o'er-shadowed with blackness, No shel-ter or help is nigh;
The depths of my sad heart are troub-led; O wak-en and save, I pray!
Earth's sun in the calm lake is mir-rored, And heaven's with-in my breast.
"Car - est Thou not that we per - ish?" How canst Thou lie a - sleep,
Tor-rents of sin and of an - guish Sweep o'er my sink - ing soul!
Lin-ger, O bless-ed Re-deem - er, Leave me a - lone no more;
When each moment so mad-ly is threat-'ning A grave in the an - gry deep?
And I per-ish! I per-ish, dear Mas-ter; O has-ten, and take con - trol!
And with joy I shall make the blest har - bor, And rest on the bliss-ful shore.

MASTER, THE TEMPEST IS RAGING

Refrain
p
pp
"The winds and the waves shall o - bey my will. Peace, . . be still!" . . .
Peace, be still! peace, be still!
Wheth-er the wrath of the storm-tossed sea, Or de - mons, or men, or what-
cres - - - - - - - - - - - - - cen - - - - - - - - - - - - - - do
ev - er it be, No wa - ter can swal-low the ship where lies The Mas-ter of
ff
o-cean and earth and skies; They all shall sweetly o - bey My will; Peace, be still!
p
p
pp
Peace, be still! They all shall sweetly o - bey My will; Peace, peace, be still!

182 PRAYER OF THANKSGIVING

ARRANGEMENT COPYRIGHT, 1928, BY HOMER A. RODEHEAVER
E. Kremser
Arr. by C. H. G.
*1. We gath - er to - geth - er to ask the Lord's blessing, He chas - tens and
2. Be - side us to guide us, our God with us join - ing, Or - dain - ing, main -
3. We all do ex - tol Thee, Thou Lead - er in bat - tle, And pray that Thou
has - tens His will to make known; The wick - ed op - press - ing
tain - ing His king - dom di - vine, So from the be - gin - ning the
still our De - fend - er wilt be. Let Thy con - gre - ga - tion es -

*1st verse by men's voices only; 2nd verse in unison; 3rd verse all parts.

PRAYER OF THANKSGIVING

rit.
cease them from distressing, Sing praises to His name, He for-gets not His
fight we were winning; Thou, Lord, wast at our side, all glo - ry be
cape trib - u - la-tion! Thy name be ev - er praised! O Lord, make us
rit.
1 & 2 Verses
3 Verse
1. own.
2. Thine!
3. free!
Lord,
make
us
A tempo
free!
fff

183 WE'RE MARCHING TO ZION

ISAAC WATTS
COPYRIGHT PROPERTY OF MARY RUNYAN LOWRY. USED BY PERMISSION
ROBERT LOWRY
Spirited
1. Come, we that love the Lord, And let our joys be known, Join
2. Let those re - fuse to sing Who nev - er knew our God; But
3. The hill of Zi - on yields A thou - sand sa - cred sweets Be -
4. Then let our songs abound, And ev - 'ry tear be dry; We're
in a song with sweet ac - cord, Join in a song with sweet accord, And
chil - dren of the heav'n-ly King, But chil - dren of the heav'nly King, May
fore we reach the heav'n-ly fields, Be-fore we reach the heav'nly fields, Or
marching thro' Immanuel's ground, We're marching thro' Immanuel's ground, To
thus sur - round the throne, And thus sur-round the throne.
speak their joys a - broad, May speak their joys a - broad.
walk the gold - en streets, Or walk the gold - en streets.
fair - er worlds on high, To fair - er worlds on high.
thus sur - round the throne, And thus sur - round the throne.
CHORUS
We're march - ing to Zi - on, Beau-ti - ful, beau-ti-ful Zi - on; We're
We're marching on to Zi - on,
march-ing upward to Zi - on, The beau - ti-ful cit - y of God.
Zi - on, Zi-on,

184 WHEN THE ROLL IS CALLED UP YONDER

J. M. B. Copyright, 1921. Renewal. Hope Publishing Co., owner J. M. BLACK

1. When the trum-pet of the Lord shall sound, and time shall be no more, And the
2. On that bright and cloudless morning when the dead in Christ shall rise, And the
3. Let us la-bor for the Mas-ter from the dawn till set-ting sun, Let us
morning breaks, e-ter-nal, bright and fair; When the saved of earth shall gather
glo-ry of His res-ur-rec-tion share; When His cho-sen ones shall gather
talk of all His wondrous love and care; Then when all of life is o-ver,
o-ver on the oth-er shore, And the roll is called up yonder, I'll be there.
to their home beyond the skies, And the roll is called up yonder, I'll be there.
and our work on earth is done, And the roll is called up yonder, I'll be there.
Fine
D.S.—roll is called up yonder, I'll be there.
CHORUS
When the roll......... is called up yon-der, When the roll......... is called up
When the roll is called up yonder, I'll be there, When the roll is called up
yon-der, When the roll........... is called up yon-der, When the
yon-der, I'll be there, When the roll is called up yon-der,
D.S.

185 OH! SUSANNA

S. C. F. | STEPHEN C. FOSTER

Moderately
1. I came to Al - a - ba - ma wid My ban - jo on my knee, I'm
2. I had a dream de od - der night, When eb - 'ry ting was still; I
3. I soon will be in New Orleans, And den I'll look all 'round, And
g'wan to Lou' - si - an - a, My true love for to see. It rain'd all night de
thought I saw Su-san - na, A - com - ing down de hill. De buckwheat cake war
when I find Su-san - na, I'll fall up - on de ground. But if I do not
day I left, De weather it was dry, De sun so hot I froze to death;
in her mouth, De tear was in her eye; Says I, I'm coming from de South,
find her, Dis dark-ie'll sure-ly die; And when I'm dead and bur - ied,
CHORUS
Su - san - na, don't you cry. Oh! Su - san - na, oh, don't you cry for
me, For I'm goin' to Lou' - si - an - a wid my ban - jo on my knee.

186 SILVER THREADS AMONG THE GOLD

EBEN E. REXFORD

H. P. DANKS

1. Dar - ling, I am grow-ing old, Sil - ver threads a-mong the gold
2. When your hair is sil - ver white, And your cheeks no lon - ger bright
3. Love can nev - er-more grow cold, Locks may lose their brown and gold;
4. Love is always young and fair; What to us is sil - ver hair,
Shine up - on my brow to - day, Life is fad- ing fast a - way;
With the ros - es of the May, I will kiss your lips and say:
Cheeks may fade and hol- low grow; But the hearts that love will know
Fad - ed cheeks or steps grown slow, To the hearts that beat be - low!
But, my darling, you will be, will be Al-ways young and fair to me;
O my darling, mine a - lone, a- lone, You have nev-er old - er grown;
Nev - er, nev- er winter's frost and chill, Summer warmth is in them still,
Since I kissed you, mine a- lone, a-lone, You have nev- er old - er grown;
CHO.—Dar-ling, I am growing, growing old, Sil- ver threads among the gold
rit.
D.S. for Chorus
Yes! my dar-ling, you will be Al-ways young and fair to me.
Yes! my dar-ling, mine a - lone, You have nev- er old- er grown.
Nev - er win-ter's frost and chill, Summer warmth is in them still.
Since I kissed you mine a - lone, You have nev -er old - er grown.
Shine up - on my brow to - day; Life is fad-ing fast a - way (a - way).

187 ROCKED IN THE CRADLE OF THE DEEP

EMMA WILLARD — JOSEPH P. KNIGHT

1. Rock'd in the cra-dle of the deep, I lay me down in peace to sleep;
2. And such the trust that still were mine, Tho' stormy winds sweep o'er the brine,
Se-cure I rest up-on the wave, For Thou, O Lord, hast pow'r to save.
Or though the tempest's fier-y breath Rouse me from sleep to wreck and death,
I know Thou wilt not slight my call, For Thou dost mark the sparrow's fall;
In o-cean cave still safe with Thee, The germ of im-mor-tal-i-ty;
And calm and peaceful is my sleep, Rocked in the cra-dle of the deep;
And calm and peaceful is my sleep, Rocked in the cra-dle of the deep.

188
SWEET AND LOW
Alfred Tennyson
Joseph Barnby
pp Larghetto
1. Sweet and low, sweet and low, Wind of the west - ern sea;
2. Sleep and rest, sleep and rest, Fa- ther will come to thee soon;
Low, low, breathe and blow, Wind of the west - ern sea;
Rest, rest, on moth - er's breast. Fa- ther will come to thee soon;
p
mf
pp
O - ver the roll - ing wa - ters go, Come from the
O - - - ver......... the wa - ters go, Come..................
Fa- ther will come to his babe in the nest, Sil - ver
Fa - - - ther...... will come to his babe, Sil - ver
f
dy - ing moon and blow, Blow him a - gain to me,
from the moon and blow,
sails all out of the west, Un - der the sil - ver moon,
sails out of......... the west,
p
rit. e dim.
pp
While my lit - tle one, while my pret - ty one sleeps......................
Sleep, my lit - tle one, sleep, my pret - ty one, sleep.......................

189 MY OLD KENTUCKY HOME
STEPHEN C. FOSTER
Rather slow
1. The sun shines bright in the old Kentuck-y home, 'Tis summer, the darkies are gay; The corn-top's ripe and the meadow's in the bloom, While the birds make mu-sic all the day. The young folks roll on the lit-tle cab-in floor, All mer-ry all hap-py and bright; By'm by hard times comes a-knocking at the door, Then my old Kentuck-y home, good-night!
2. They hunt no more for the pos-sum and the coon, On the meadow, the hill and the shore; They sing no more by the glim-mer of the moon, On the bench by the old cab-in door. The day goes by like a shad-ow o'er the heart, With sor-row where all was de-light; The time has come when the darkies have to part, Then my old Kentuck-y home, good-night!
3. The head must bow and the back will have to bend, Wher-ev-er the dark-ey may go; A few more days, and the trou-ble all will end, In the field where the sug-ar canes grow; A few more days for to tote the wea-ry load,—No mat-ter 'twill nev-er be light; A few more days till we tot-ter on the road, Then my old Kentuck-y home, good-night!

MY OLD KENTUCKY HOME
Refrain
Weep no more, my la-dy, Oh! weep no more to-day! We will sing one song for the
old Ken-tuck-y home, For the old Kentuck-y home, far a-way.
190
LONG, LONG AGO
T. H. B.
Thomas H. Bayly
Moderately
1. Tell me the tales that to me were so dear, Long, long a-go, Long, long a-go;
2. Do you remember the path where we met, Long, long a-go, Long, long a-go?
3. Tho' by your kindness my fond hopes were rais'd, Long, long a-go, Long, long a-go,
Fine
Sing me the songs I de-light-ed to hear, Long, long a-go, long a-go.
Ah, yes, you told me you ne'er would forget, Long, long a-go, long a-go.
You by more el-oquent lips have been prais'd, Long, long a-go, long a-go.
D.S.-Let me be-lieve that you love as you lov'd, Long, long a-go, long a-go.
D.S.-Still my heart treasures the prais-es, I heard, Long, long a-go, long a-go.
D.S.-Blest as I was when I sat by your side, Long, long a-go, long a-go.
D.S.
Now you are come all my grief is removed, Let me forget that so long you have rov'd,
Then, to all oth-ers my smile you prefer'd, Love, when you spoke, gave a charm to each word,
But by long absence your truth has been tried, Still to your accents I listen with pride,

DARLING NELLIE GRAY

1. There's a low, green val-ley on the old Ken-tuck-y shore, Where I've
2. When the moon had climb'd the mountain, and the stars were shining too, Then I'd
3. My eyes are get-ting blind-ed, and I can not see my way; Hark! there's
whiled man-y hap-py hours a-way, A - sit-ting and a-sing-ing by the
take my dar-ling Nel-lie Gray, And we'd float down the riv-er in my
some-bod-y knocking at the door, Oh, I hear the an-gels call-ing, and I
lit-tle cot-tage door Where lived my dar-ling Nel-lie Gray.
lit-tle red ca-noe, While my ban-jo sweet-ly I would play.
see my Nel-lie Gray, Fare-well to the old Ken-tuck-y shore.
CHORUS
1–2. O my poor Nel-lie Gray, they have tak-en you a-way, And I'll
3. O my dar-ling Nel-lie Gray, up in heav-en there, they say, That they'll
nev-er see my dar-ling an-y more; I'm sit-ting on the riv-er and I'm
nev-er take you from me an-y more; I'm a coming—coming—coming, as the

DARLING NELLIE GRAY

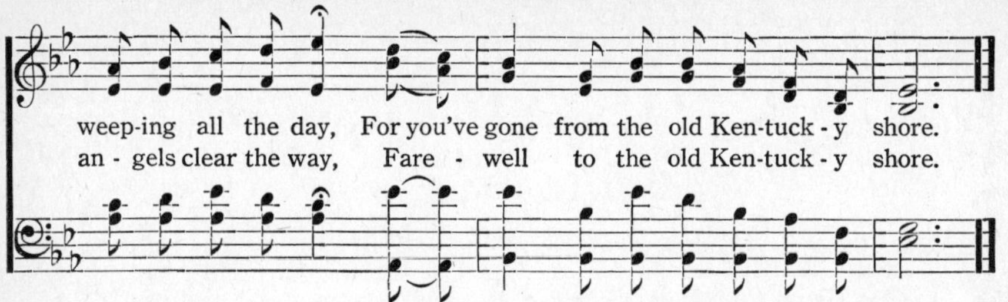
weep-ing all the day, For you've gone from the old Ken-tuck-y shore.
an - gels clear the way, Fare - well to the old Ken-tuck-y shore.

192 DRINK TO ME ONLY WITH THINE EYES

BEN JONSON

Old English Air

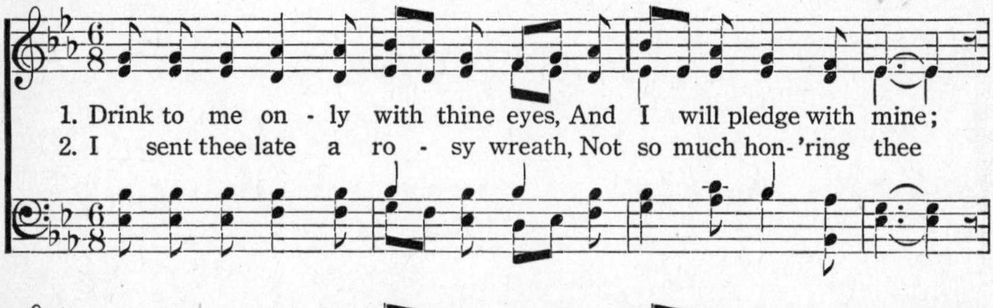

1. Drink to me on - ly with thine eyes, And I will pledge with mine;
2. I sent thee late a ro - sy wreath, Not so much hon-'ring thee

Or leave a kiss with - in the cup, And I'll not ask for wine;
As giv - ing it a hope that there It could not with - ered be;

The thirst, that from the soul doth rise, Doth ask a drink di - vine;
But thou there - on didst on - ly breathe, And sent'st it back to me,

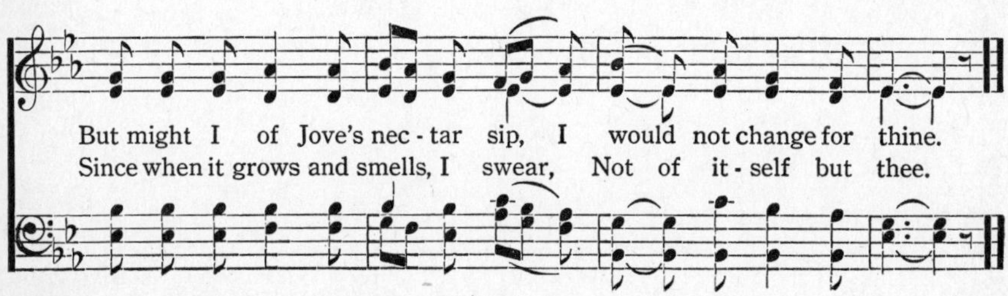

But might I of Jove's nec - tar sip, I would not change for thine.
Since when it grows and smells, I swear, Not of it - self but thee.

193 THE OLD OAKEN BUCKET

Samuel Woodworth
F. Kaillmark
1. { How dear to my heart are the scenes of my child-hood,
The or-chard, the mead-ow, the deep tan-gled wild-wood,
2. { The moss-cov-ered buck-et I hailed as a treas-ure,
I found it the source of an ex-quis-ite pleas-ure,
3. { How sweet from the green, mos-sy brim to re-ceive it,
Not a full-blush-ing gob-let could tempt me to leave it,
D.C.—The old oak-en buck-et, the i-ron bound buck-et,
Fine
When fond rec-ol-lec-tion pre-sents them to view! }
And ev-'ry loved spot which my in-fan-cy knew; }
For oft-en at noon, when re-turned from the field, }
The pur-est and sweet-est that na-ture can yield. }
As, poised on the curb, it in-clined to my lips! }
Tho' filled with the nec-tar that Ju-pi-ter sips. }
The moss-cov-ered buck-et that hung from the well.
The wide-spreading pond, and the mill that stood by it, The bridge and the
How ar-dent I seized it with hands that were glow-ing, And quick to the
And now, far re-mov'd from the lov'd hab-i-ta-tion, The tear of re-
rock where the cat-a-ract fell; The cot of my fa-ther, the
white peb-bled bot-tom it fell; Then soon, with the em-blem of
gret will in-tru-sive-ly swell As fan-cy re-verts to my

THE OLD OAKEN BUCKET
D.C. al Fine
dai - ry house nigh it, And e'en the rude buck-et that hung in the well.
truth o - ver-flow - ing, And drip-ping with cool-ness it rose from the well.
fa - ther's plan- ta - tion, And sighs for the buck - et that hung in the well.
194 THE VACANT CHAIR
H. S. WASHBURN
GEORGE F. ROOT
With feeling
1. We shall meet, but we shall miss him, There will be one va - cant chair;
2. At our fire - side sad and lone - ly, Oft - en will the bos - om swell
3. True, they tell us wreaths of glo - ry Ev - er - more will deck his brow,
D.C.—We shall meet, but we shall miss him, There will be one va-cant chair;
Fine
We shall lin - ger to ca - ress him, When we breathe our ev'n - ing pray'r.
At remembrance of the sto - ry How our no - ble Wil - lie fell;
But this soothes the anguish on - ly Sweep - ing o'er our heart strings now.
We shall lin - ger to ca- ress him, When we breathe our ev'n - ing pray'r.
When a year a - go we gathered, Joy was in his mild blue eye,
How he strove to bear our ban- ner Thro' the thick - est of the fight,
Sleep to - day, O ear - ly fall - en, In thy green and nar- row bed;
D.C. al Fine
But a gold - en cord is sev-ered, And our hopes in ru - in lie.
And up-hold our country's hon - or In the strength of manhood's might.
Dir - ges from the pine and cy-press Min- gle with the tears we shed.

195 POLLY-WOLLY-DOODLE

Moderato
1. Oh, I went down South for to see my Sal, Sing Pol - ly- wol- ly -
2. Oh, my Sal, she am a maid - en fair, Sing Pol - ly- wol- ly -
3. I came to a riv-er and couldn't get across, Sing Pol - ly- wol- ly -
4. A grass hop-per sit-ting on a rail - road track, Sing Pol - ly- wol- ly -
doo- dle all the day; My Sal - ly am a spunk- y gal, Sing
doo- dle all the day; With cur - ly eyes and laugh - ing hair, Sing
doo- dle all the day, I jumped on a nigger and tho't he was a hoss, Sing
doo- dle all the day, A - pick - ing his teeth with a carpet tack, Sing
Pol - ly- wol - ly - doo- dle all the day.
CHORUS
Fare thee well, fare thee
Fare - well,
well, Fare thee well, my fair - y fay, For I'm goin' to Louis-i - an - na,
fare - well,
For to see my Su - sy - an - na, Sing Pol - ly- wol - ly-doo- dle all the day.

SOLOMON LEVI

College Song

My name is Sol - o - mon Le - vi, And my store's on Sa - lem street; That's
where to buy your coats and vests And ev'rything else that's neat; Sec-ond-hand-ed
ul-ster-ettes And o - ver-coats so fine, For all the boys that trade with me At
Tra-la - la - la - la - la -
Fine.
Hundred and For - ty - nine. O Sol - o - mon Le - vi, Tra - la-la - la -
la, Tra - la - la - la - la - la - la - la - la - la,
D.S. al Fine.
la. Poor Sol - lie Le - vi, Tra-la - la - la - la - la - la - la - la, My
la-la, My

197 O DEM GOLDEN SLIPPERS

J. A. BLAND

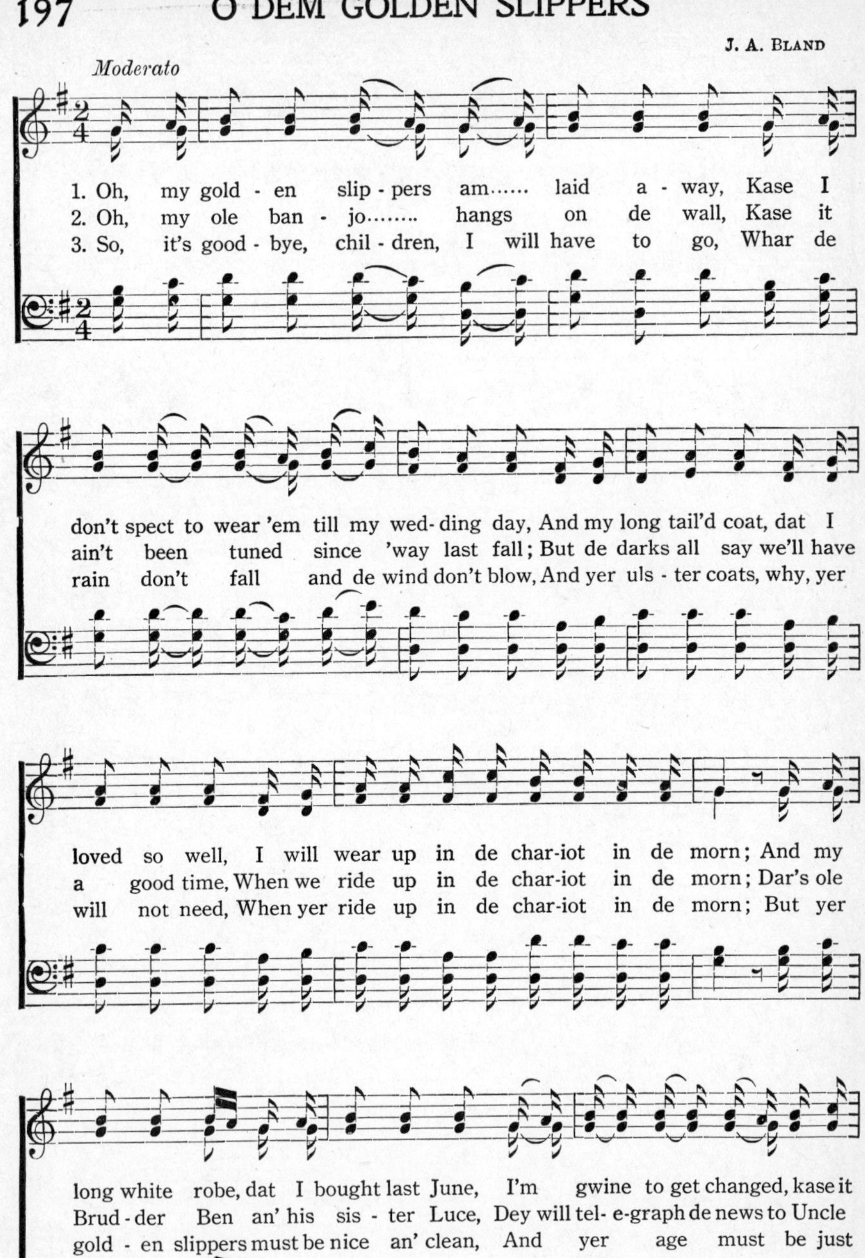
Moderato
1. Oh, my gold - en slip - pers am...... laid a - way, Kase I
2. Oh, my ole ban - jo........ hangs on de wall, Kase it
3. So, it's good - bye, chil - dren, I will have to go, Whar de
don't spect to wear 'em till my wed- ding day, And my long tail'd coat, dat I
ain't been tuned since 'way last fall; But de darks all say we'll have
rain don't fall and de wind don't blow, And yer uls - ter coats, why, yer
loved so well, I will wear up in de char-iot in de morn; And my
a good time, When we ride up in de char-iot in de morn; Dar's ole
will not need, When yer ride up in de char-iot in de morn; But yer
long white robe, dat I bought last June, I'm gwine to get changed, kase it
Brud - der Ben an' his sis - ter Luce, Dey will tel- e-graph de news to Uncle
gold - en slippers must be nice an' clean, And yer age must be just

O DEM GOLDEN SLIPPERS

fits too soon, And de old gray hoss dat I used to drive, I will
Bac - co Juice, What a great camp-meet-in' der will be dat day, When we
sweet six - teen, And yer white kid gloves yer will have to wear, When yer
CHORUS
mf Repeat pp
hitch him to de chariot in de morn.
ride up in de chariot in de morn.
ride up in de chariot in de morn.
O dem gold - en slip-pers, O dem
gold - en slippers! Gold- en slippers I'se gwine to wear, be-kase dey look so
neat; O dem gold - en slip-pers, O dem gold - en slip-pers,
so neat.
Gold - en slip-pers I'se gwine to wear, To walk de gold- en street.

198 HOME, SWEET HOME
JOHN HOWARD PAYNE
HENRY R. BISHOP
1. 'Mid pleasures and pal - a - ces tho' we may roam, Be it ev - er so hum - ble, there's no place like home; A charm from the skies seems to hal - low us there, Which, seek thro' the world, is ne'er met with elsewhere.
2. I gaze on the moon as I tread the drear wild, And feel that my moth - er now thinks of her child, As she looks on that moon from our own cottage door, Thro' the woodbine whose fragrance shall cheer me no more.
3. An ex - ile from home splendor daz-zles in vain; Oh, give me my low - ly thatch'd cot - tage a - gain; The birds sing- ing gai - ly, that came at my call, Give me them, and that peace of mind dear - er than all.
REFRAIN
Home, home, sweet, sweet home, There's no place like home, There's no place like home.
199 GOOD-NIGHT, LADIES
Sostenuto
f
1. Good-night, la - dies! Good-night, la - dies! Good-night, la - dies! We're
2. Fare- well, la - dies! Fare- well, la - dies! Fare- well, la - dies! We're
3. Sweet dreams, la - dies! Sweet dreams, la - dies! Sweet dreams, la - dies! We're

GOOD-NIGHT, LADIES

Allegro
Repeat pp
rit. molto
1
2
going to leave you now. Merrily we roll along, roll along, roll along, O'er the dark blue sea.
200
OLD BLACK JOE
S. C. F.
STEPHEN C. FOSTER
1. Gone are the days when my heart was young and gay; Gone are my friends from the cot-ton fields a-way; Gone from the earth to a bet-ter land I know, I hear their gen-tle voic-es call-ing, "Old Black Joe."
2. Why do I weep when my heart should feel no pain? Why do I sigh that my friends come not a-gain? Griev-ing for forms now de-part-ed long a-go, I hear their gen-tle voic-es call-ing, "Old Black Joe."
3. Where are the hearts once so hap-py and so free? The chil-dren so dear that I held up-on my knee? Gone to the shore where my soul has long'd to go, I hear their gen-tle voic-es call-ing, "Old Black Joe."
Fine
CHORUS
D.S. al Fine
I'm com-ing, I'm com-ing, For my head is bend-ing low;

201 FLOW GENTLY, SWEET AFTON
ROBERT BURNS
JAMES SPILMAN
Not too slowly
1. Flow gen-tly, sweet Af-ton, amang thy green braes; Flow gently, I'll sing thee a
2. How loft - y, sweet Af-ton, thy neighboring hills, Far mark'd with the courses of
3. Thy crystal stream, Af-ton, how love-ly it glides, And winds by the cot where my
song in thy praise; My Mary's asleep by thy murmuring stream, Flow gently, sweet
clear winding rills! There daily I wan-der, as morn ris - es high, My flocks and my
Ma - ry resides! How wanton thy waters her snow - y feet lave, As, gath'ring sweet
Af - ton, dis- turb not her dream. Thou stock-dove whose echo resounds from the
Ma - ry's sweet cot in my eye. How pleasant thy banks and green valleys be -
flow'rets, she stems thy clear wave! Flow gen- tly, sweet Af - ton, amang thy green
hill, Ye wild whistling black-birds in yon thorny dell, Thou green-crested
low, Where wild in the woodlands the prim-ros- es blow! There oft, as mild
braes, Flow gen- tly, sweet riv - er, the theme of my lays: My Ma-ry's a -
lap-wing, thy screaming for-bear, I charge you, disturb not my slumbering fair.
eve-ning creeps o - ver the lea, The sweet scented birk shades my Mary and me.
sleep by thy murmuring stream, Flow gently, sweet Afton, disturb not her dream.

202 WHEN YOU AND I WERE YOUNG, MAGGIE

GEORGE W. JOHNSON | J. A. BUTTERFIELD

1. I wander'd to-day to the hill, Maggie, To watch the scene be - low,
2. A cit - y so si - lent and lone, Maggie, Where the young and the gay and the best,
3. They say I am fee - ble with age, Maggie, My steps are less sprightly than then;

The creek and the old rusty mill, Maggie, Where we sat in the long, long a - go.
In polish'd white mansion of stone, Maggie, Have each found a place of rest,
My face is a well-written page, Maggie, But time a - lone was the pen.

The green grove is gone from the hill, Maggie, Where first the dai - sies sprung;
Is built where the birds used to play, Maggie, And join in the songs that were sung;
They say we are a - ged and gray, Maggie, As spray by the white breakers flung;

D.S.–And now we are a - ged and gray, Mag-gie, The tri - als of life nearly done,

D.S.

The old rust - y mill is still, Maggie, Since you and I were young.
For we sang just as gay as they, Maggie, When you and I were young.
But to me you're as fair as you were, Maggie, When you and I were young.

Let us sing of the days that are gone, Maggie, When you and I were young.

203
JUANITA
Caroline Norton
Spanish Melody
1. Soft o'er the fountain, Ling'ring falls the southern moon; Far o'er the mountain
2. When in thy dreaming Moons like these shall shine again, And daylight beaming
Breaks the day too soon! In thy dark eyes' splendor, Where the warm light loves to dwell,
Prove thy dreams are vain, Wilt thou not, relenting, For thine ab-sent lov-er sigh?
Wea-ry looks, yet ten-der, Speak their fond farewell, Ni-ta! Jua-ni-ta!
In thy heart con-sent-ing To a pray'r gone by? Ni-ta! Jua-ni-ta!
Ask thy soul if we should part! Ni-ta! Jua-ni-ta! Lean thou on my heart.
Let me lin-ger by thy side! Ni-ta! Jua-ni-ta! Be my own fair bride.
3
204
MY BONNIE
H. J. F.
H. J. Fuller
1. My Bon-nie is o-ver the o-cean, My Bon-nie is o-ver the sea,
2. Oh! blow, ye winds, o-ver the o-cean, And blow, ye winds, o-ver the sea,
3. Last night as I lay on my pil-low, Last night as I lay on my bed,

MY BONNIE
My Bon- nie is o- ver the o - cean; Oh! bring back my Bonnie to me.
Oh! blow ye winds, o- ver the o - cean, And bring back my Bonnie to me.
Last night, as I lay on my pil - low, I dreamed that my Bonnie was dead.
CHORUS
Bring back, bring back, Bring back my Bon - nie to me, to me;
Bring back, bring back, Oh! bring back my Bon - nie to me.
205
CLEMENTINE
1. In a cav- ern, by a can - yon, Ex - ca - vat - ing for a mine,
2. Light she was and like a fair - y, And her shoes were number nine,
3. Drove she duck- lings to the wa - ter Ev - 'ry morn- ing just at nine,
4. Ros - y lips a - bove the wa - ter, Blow- ing bub- bles might - y fine,
5. How I missed her! how I missed her! How I missed my Clem - en- tine!
Dwelt a min - er, for - ty - nin - er, And his daugh - ter, Clem- en - tine.
Herr- ing box - es with- out top - ses, San- dals were for Clem- en - tine.
Struck her foot a - gainst a splin - ter, Fell in - to the foam- ing brine.
But, a - las! I was no swim- mer, So I lost my Clem- en - tine.
But I kissed her lit - tle sis - ter, And for - got my Clem- en - tine.
ff CHORUS
O my dar - ling, O my dar - ling, O my dar - ling Clem- en - tine,
Thou art lost and gone for - ev - er, Dread- ful sor - ry, Clem- en- tine.

206
AULD LANG SYNE
Robert Burns
Scotch Air
1. Should auld acquaintance be for-got, And nev - er bro't to mind? Should auld ac-quaintance be for-got, And days of auld lang syne?
2. We twa ha'e ran a - boot the braes, And pu'd the gowans fine, We've wander'd mony a wea - ry foot Sin' auld lang syne.
3. And here's a hand, my trust - y frien', And gie's a hand o' thine; We'll tak' a cup o' kindness yet, For auld lang syne.
Refrain
For auld lang syne, my dear, For auld lang syne; We'll tak' a cup o' kindness yet For auld lang syne.
207
SEEING NELLIE HOME
p
Andante
1. In the sky the bright stars glit - tered, On the bank the pale moon shone;
2. On my arm a soft hand rest - ed, Rest - ed light as o - cean foam;
3. On my lips a whis - per trem - bled, Trembled till it dared to come;
4. On my life new hopes were dawn-ing, And those hopes have liv'd and grown;
cres.
dim.
And 'twas from Aunt Dinah's quilting par - ty, I was see - ing Nel- lie home.

SEEING NELLIE HOME

208

OLD FOLKS AT HOME

SEEING NELLIE HOME
REFRAIN
I was see-ing Nel-lie home, I was see-ing Nel-lie home;
dim. e rit.
And 'twas from Aunt Dinah's quilting par-ty, I was see-ing Nel-lie home.
208
OLD FOLKS AT HOME
S. C. F.
STEPHEN C. FOSTER
1. Way down up-on de Swa-nee Riv-er, Far, far a-way,
All up and down de whole cre-a-tion. Sad-ly I roam,
2. All roun' de lit-tle farm I wander'd, When I was young;
When I was play-ing wid my broth-er, Hap-py was I;
3. One lit-tle hut a-mong de bush-es, One dat I love,
When will I see de bees a-humming All roun' de comb?
Fine
Dere's wha my heart is turn-ing ev-er, Dere's wha de old folks stay.
Still long-ing for de old plan-ta-tion, And for de old folks at home.
Den man-y hap-py days I squander'd, Man-y de songs I sung.
Oh! take me to my kind old moth-er, Dere let me live and die.
Still sad-ly to my mem-'ry rush-es, No mat-ter where I rove.
When will I hear de ban-jo tumming, Down in my good old home?
D.S.—O dark-ies, how my heart grows weary, Far from de old folks at home.
CHORUS
D.S.
All de world am sad and drear-y, Ev-'ry-where I roam;

209 THE FIRST NOEL

Words Traditional
Air Traditional
mf
1. The first No - el the an - gel did say Was to cer - tain poor shepherds in fields as they lay: In fields where they lay, keep-ing their sheep On a cold win-ter's night that was so deep.
2. They look - ed up and saw a star, Shin - ing in the East be - yond them far, And to the earth it gave great light, And so it con - tin-ued both day and night.
3. This star drew nigh to the north-west, O'er Beth - le - hem it took its rest, And there it did both stop and stay Right o - ver the place where Je - sus lay.
4. Then en - ter'd in there Wise Men three, Full rev - 'rent-ly up - on their knee, And of - fer'd there in His pres - ence Their gold and myrrh and frank - in - cense.
ff CHORUS
No - el, No - el, No - el, No - el, Born is the King of Is - ra - el.
210
SILENT NIGHT
Joseph Möhr
Franz Gruber
pp
1. Si - lent night! Ho - ly night! All is calm, all is bright Round yon
2. Si - lent night! Ho - ly night! Shepherds quake at the sight! Glo - ries
3. Si - lent night! Ho - ly night! Son of God, love's pure light Ra - diant

SILENT NIGHT

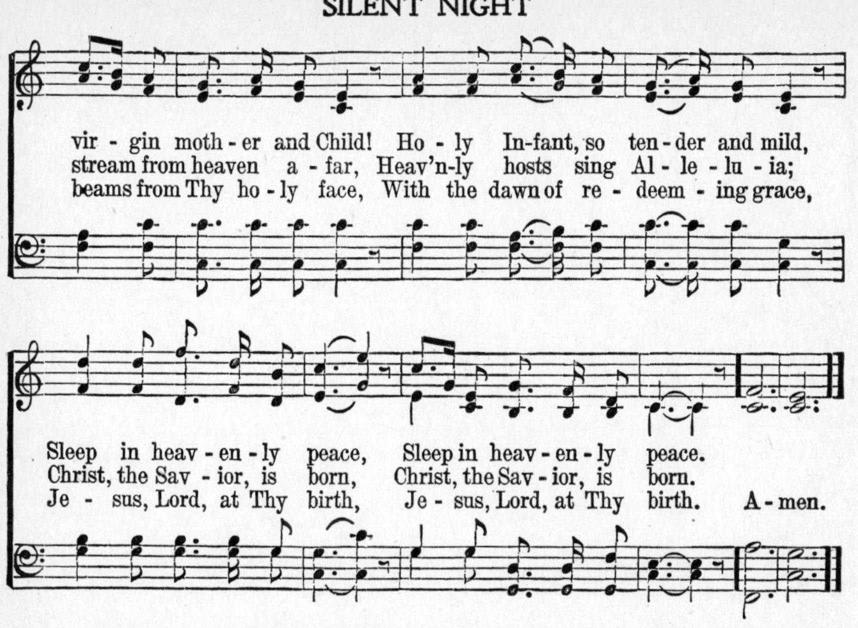
vir - gin moth - er and Child! Ho - ly In-fant, so ten - der and mild,
stream from heaven a - far, Heav'n-ly hosts sing Al - le - lu - ia;
beams from Thy ho - ly face, With the dawn of re - deem - ing grace,
Sleep in heav - en - ly peace, Sleep in heav - en - ly peace.
Christ, the Sav - ior, is born, Christ, the Sav - ior, is born.
Je - sus, Lord, at Thy birth, Je - sus, Lord, at Thy birth. A - men.

211 WHILE SHEPHERDS WATCHED THEIR FLOCKS

Nahum Tate — CHRISTMAS C. M. — George F. Handel

1. While shepherds watched their flocks by night, All seat-ed on the ground, The an-gel
2. "Fear not," said he; for might-y dread Had seized their troubled mind, "Glad tidings
3. "To you, in Da-vid's town, this day Is born, of Da-vid's line, The Sav-ior,
4. "The heav'nly Babe you there shall find To hu-man view dis-played, All mean-ly
5. "All glo - ry be to God on high, And to the earth be peace; Good-will hence-

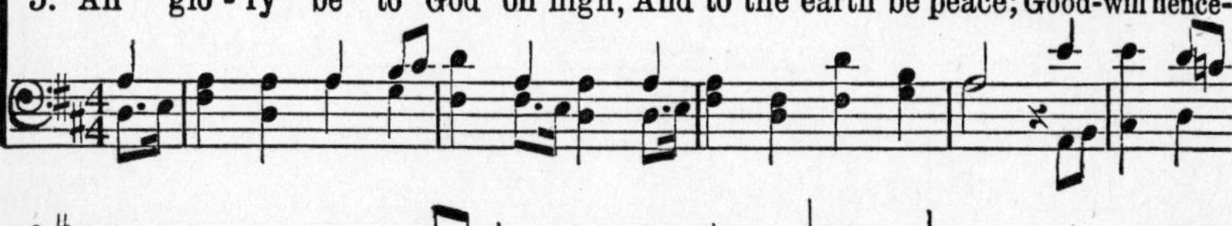

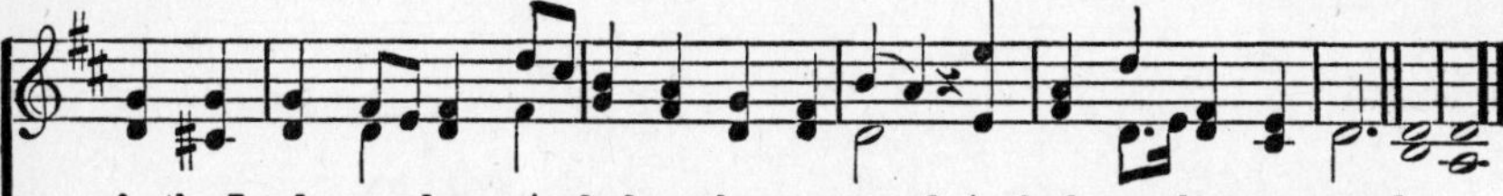

of the Lord came down, And glory shone a-round, And glo-ry shone a-round.
of great joy I bring, To you and all mankind, To you and all mankind.
who is Christ the Lord; And this shall be the sign, And this shall be the sign:
wrapped in swathing bands, And in a man-ger laid, And in a man-ger laid."
forth from heav'n to men Be-gin, and never cease, Be-gin, and never cease!" AMEN.

212 HARK! THE HERALD ANGELS SING

CHARLES WESLEY

MENDELSSOHN

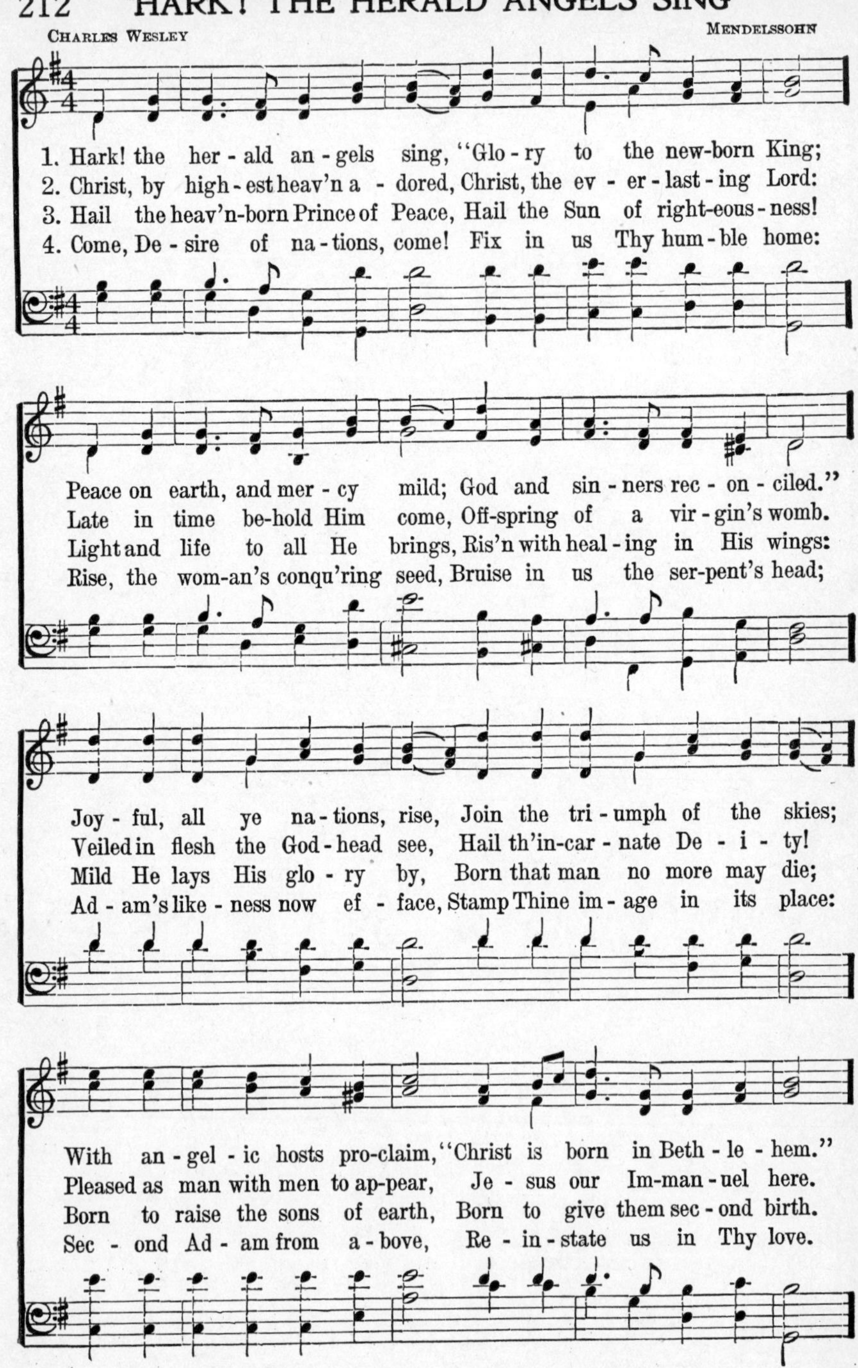
1. Hark! the her - ald an - gels sing, "Glo - ry to the new-born King;
2. Christ, by high - est heav'n a - dored, Christ, the ev - er - last - ing Lord:
3. Hail the heav'n-born Prince of Peace, Hail the Sun of right-eous - ness!
4. Come, De - sire of na - tions, come! Fix in us Thy hum - ble home:
Peace on earth, and mer - cy mild; God and sin - ners rec - on - ciled."
Late in time be-hold Him come, Off-spring of a vir - gin's womb.
Light and life to all He brings, Ris'n with heal - ing in His wings:
Rise, the wom-an's conqu'ring seed, Bruise in us the ser-pent's head;
Joy - ful, all ye na - tions, rise, Join the tri - umph of the skies;
Veiled in flesh the God - head see, Hail th'in-car - nate De - i - ty!
Mild He lays His glo - ry by, Born that man no more may die;
Ad - am's like - ness now ef - face, Stamp Thine im - age in its place:
With an - gel - ic hosts pro-claim, "Christ is born in Beth - le - hem."
Pleased as man with men to ap-pear, Je - sus our Im-man - uel here.
Born to raise the sons of earth, Born to give them sec - ond birth.
Sec - ond Ad - am from a - bove, Re - in - state us in Thy love.

HARK! THE HERALD ANGELS SING
Hark! the her - ald an-gels sing, "Glo - ry to the new-born King." Amen.
213 O COME, ALL YE FAITHFUL
Tr. by FREDERICK OAKELEY
WADE'S Cantus Diversi
1. O come, all ye faith - ful, joy - ful and tri - um-phant, O come ye, O come ye to Beth - le - hem; Come and be - hold Him, born the King of an - gels.
2. Sing, choirs of an - gels, sing in ex - ul - ta - tion, O sing, all ye bright hosts of heav'n a - bove; Glo - ry to God, all glo - ry in the high-est.
3. Yea, Lord, we greet Thee, born this hap - py morn-ing, Je - sus, to Thee be all glo - ry giv'n; Word of the Fa - ther, now in flesh ap - pear-ing.
REFRAIN
O come, let us a-dore Him, O come, let us a - dore Him, O come, let us a - dore Him, Christ, the Lord. A - men.

214 O LITTLE TOWN OF BETHLEHEM

PHILLIPS BROOKS | LEWIS H. REDNER

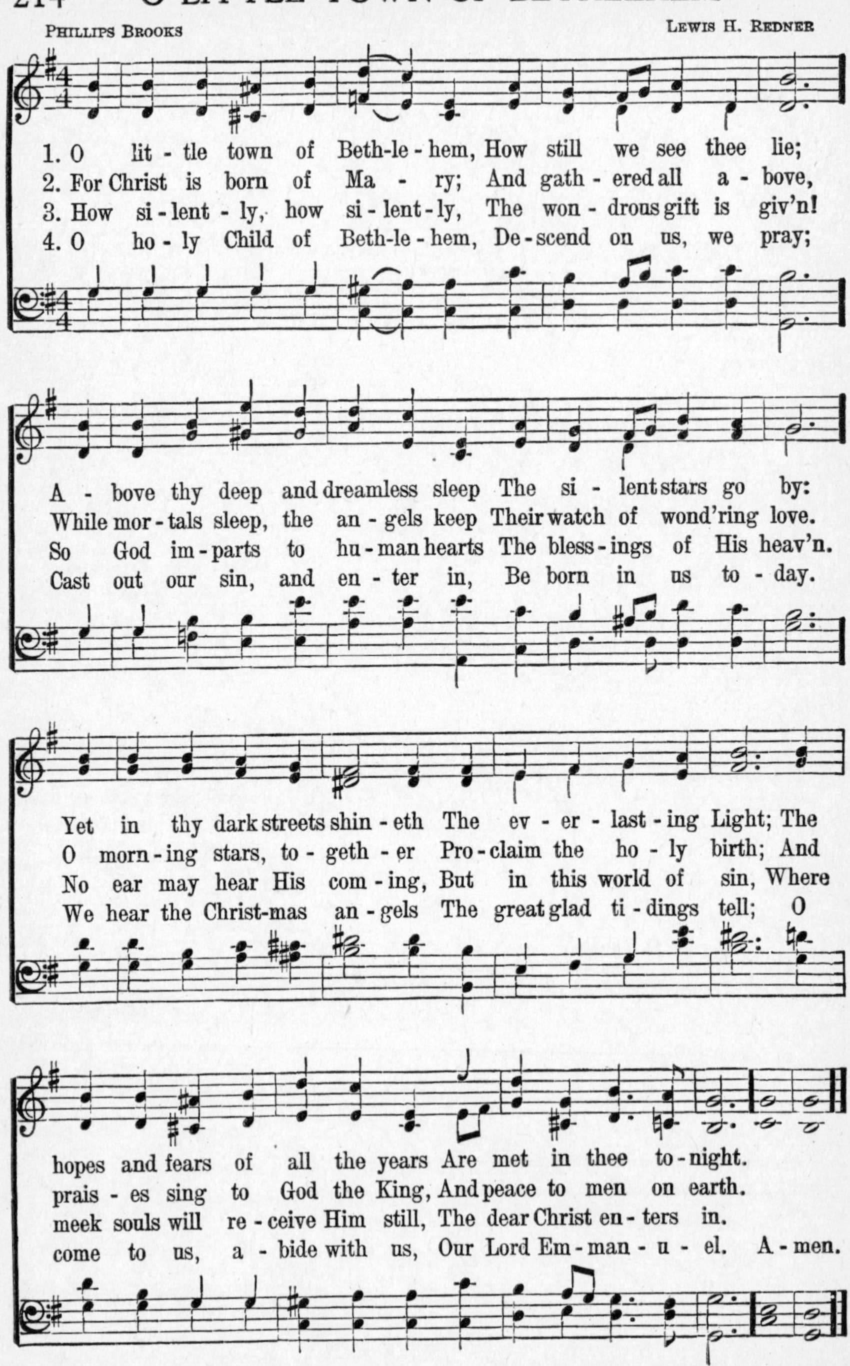
1. O lit - tle town of Beth-le - hem, How still we see thee lie;
2. For Christ is born of Ma - ry; And gath - ered all a - bove,
3. How si - lent - ly, how si - lent - ly, The won - drous gift is giv'n!
4. O ho - ly Child of Beth-le - hem, De - scend on us, we pray;
A - bove thy deep and dreamless sleep The si - lent stars go by:
While mor - tals sleep, the an - gels keep Their watch of wond'ring love.
So God im - parts to hu - man hearts The bless - ings of His heav'n.
Cast out our sin, and en - ter in, Be born in us to - day.
Yet in thy dark streets shin - eth The ev - er - last - ing Light; The
O morn - ing stars, to - geth - er Pro - claim the ho - ly birth; And
No ear may hear His com - ing, But in this world of sin, Where
We hear the Christ-mas an - gels The great glad ti - dings tell; O
hopes and fears of all the years Are met in thee to - night.
prais - es sing to God the King, And peace to men on earth.
meek souls will re - ceive Him still, The dear Christ en - ters in.
come to us, a - bide with us, Our Lord Em - man - u - el. A - men.

215 IT CAME UPON THE MIDNIGHT CLEAR

EDMUND H. SEARS | RICHARD S. WILLIS

1. It came up - on the mid-night clear, That glo-rious song of old,
2. Still thro' the clo-ven skies they come, With peaceful wings un - furled,
3. And ye, be - neath life's crushing load, Whose forms are bending low,
4. For lo, the days are has - t'ning on, By prophet bards fore-told,

From an - gels bending near the earth To touch their harps of gold:
And still their heav'nly mu - sic floats O'er all the wea - ry world:
Who toil a - long the climb - ing way With pain - ful steps and slow,
When with the ev - er - cir - cling years Comes 'round the age of gold:

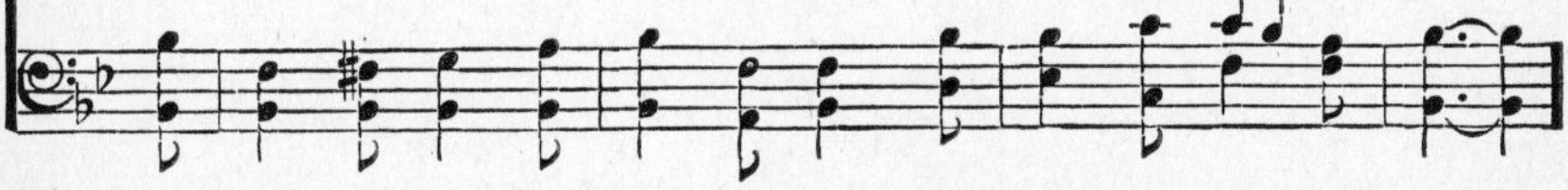

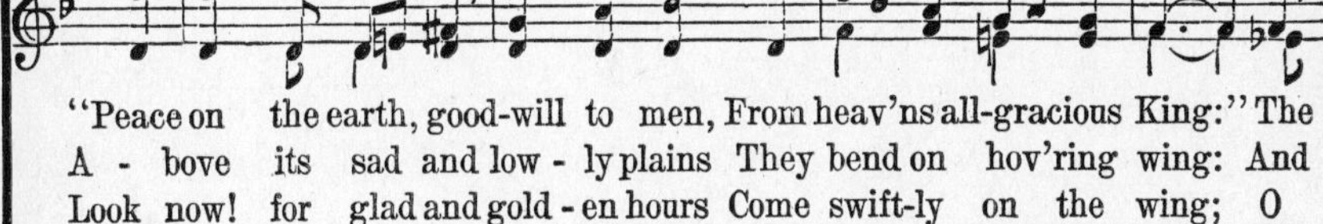

"Peace on the earth, good-will to men, From heav'ns all-gracious King:" The
A - bove its sad and low - ly plains They bend on hov'ring wing: And
Look now! for glad and gold - en hours Come swift-ly on the wing; O
When peace shall o - ver all the earth Its an - cient splendors fling, And

world in sol - emn still-ness lay To hear the an - gels sing.
ev - er o'er its Ba - bel sounds The bless-ed an - gels sing.
rest be - side the wea - ry road, And hear the an - gels sing.
the whole world give back the song Which now the an - gels sing. A - men.

216 JOY TO THE WORLD!

Isaac Watts | George F. Handel

1. Joy to the world! the Lord is come; Let earth re - ceive her King; Let ev - 'ry heart pre - pare Him room, And heav'n and na - ture sing, And heav'n and na - ture sing, And heav'n, and heav'n and na - ture sing.
2. Joy to the earth! the Sav - ior reigns; Let men their songs em - ploy; While fields and floods, rocks, hills and plains Re - peat the sound - ing joy, Re - peat the sound - ing joy, Re - peat, re - peat the sound - ing joy.
3. No more let sins and sor - rows grow, Nor thorns in - fest the ground; He comes to make His bless - ings flow Far as the curse is found, Far as the curse is found, Far as, far as the curse is found.
4. He rules the world with truth and grace, And makes the na - tions prove The glo - ries of His right-eous - ness, And won - ders of His love, And won - ders of His love, And won-ders, and won - ders of His love.
1. And heav'n and na - ture sing, And heav'n and na - ture sing,

217 CROWN HIM WITH MANY CROWNS

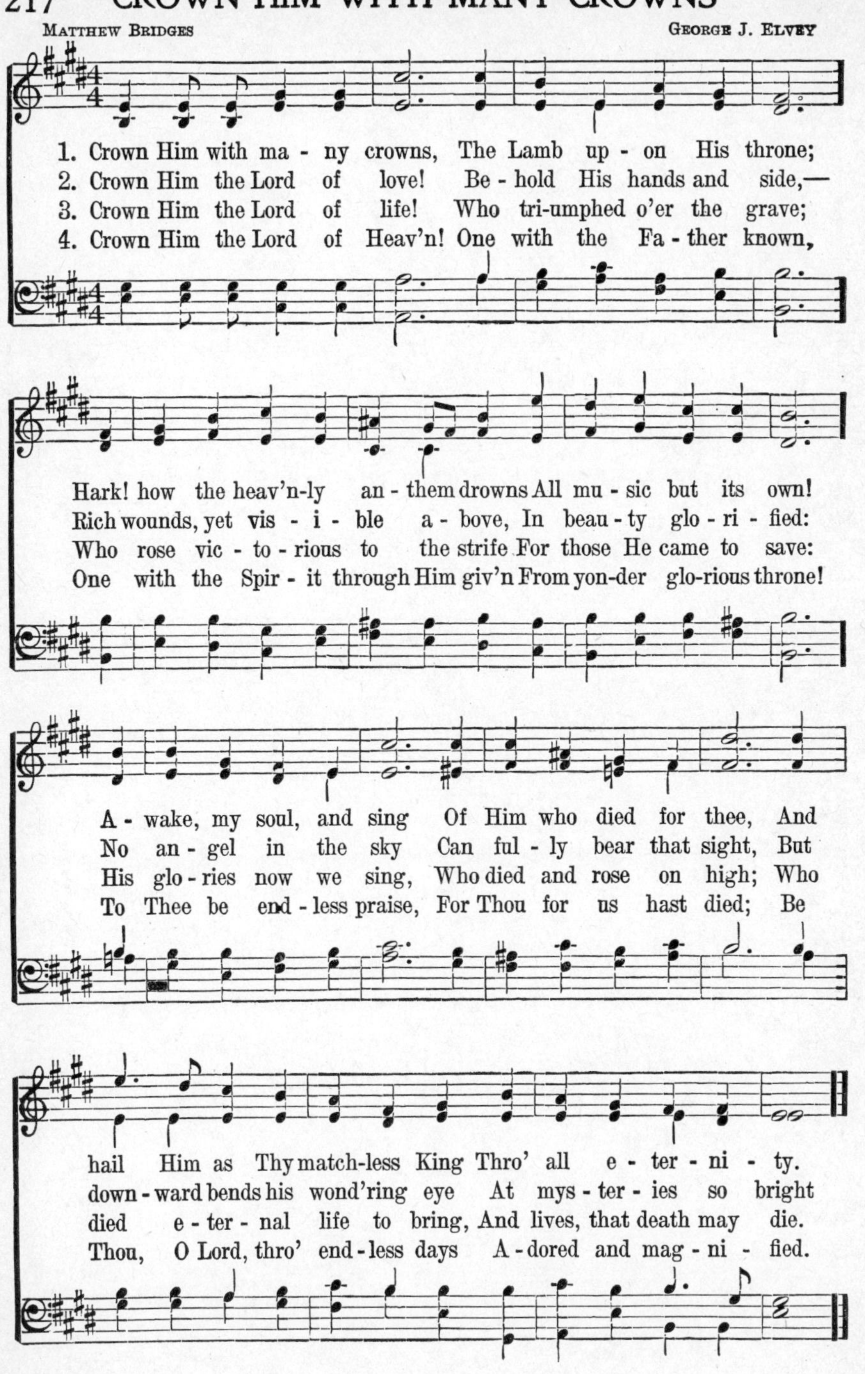
MATTHEW BRIDGES
GEORGE J. ELVEY
1. Crown Him with ma - ny crowns, The Lamb up - on His throne;
2. Crown Him the Lord of love! Be - hold His hands and side,—
3. Crown Him the Lord of life! Who tri-umphed o'er the grave;
4. Crown Him the Lord of Heav'n! One with the Fa - ther known,
Hark! how the heav'n-ly an - them drowns All mu - sic but its own!
Rich wounds, yet vis - i - ble a - bove, In beau - ty glo - ri - fied:
Who rose vic - to - rious to the strife For those He came to save:
One with the Spir - it through Him giv'n From yon-der glo-rious throne!
A - wake, my soul, and sing Of Him who died for thee, And
No an - gel in the sky Can ful - ly bear that sight, But
His glo - ries now we sing, Who died and rose on high; Who
To Thee be end - less praise, For Thou for us hast died; Be
hail Him as Thy match-less King Thro' all e - ter - ni - ty.
down - ward bends his wond'ring eye At mys - ter - ies so bright
died e - ter - nal life to bring, And lives, that death may die.
Thou, O Lord, thro' end - less days A - dored and mag - ni - fied.

THE PALMS

Arr. by C. H. G.

1. O'er all the way green palms and blossoms gay Are strewn this day in festival
2. His word goes forth, and peo-ple by its might Once more their freedom gain from
3. Sing and re-joice, O blest Je - ru - sa - lem, Of all thy songs sing the e-
prep - a - ra - tion, Where Je - sus comes, to wipe our tears a - way;
deg - ra - da - tion; Hu - man - i - ty doth give to each his right,
man - ci - pa - tion; Thro' bound-less love, the Christ of Beth - le - hem
RESPONSE
E'en now the throng to welcome Him prepare. Join, sing His name di-vine,
While those in darkness find restored the light.
Brings forth the hope to thee for - ev - er-more. Join all, and sing Ho - san - na!
Let ev - 'ry voice resound with u - nit - ed ac - cla-ma - tion, Ho-san - -
Praised be the
na! Praised be the Lord, Bless Him who cometh to bring us sal-va - tion.
Lord, Ho-san - na!

219 CHRIST, THE LORD, IS RISEN TODAY

CHARLES WESLEY — WORGAN — From LYRA DAVIDICA

1. Christ the Lord is ris'n to - day, Al - le - lu - ia!
2. Lives a - gain our glo - rious King: Al - le - lu - ia!
3. Love's re - deem - ing work is done, Al - le - lu - ia!
4. Soar we now, where Christ has led, Al - le - lu - ia!
Sons of men and an - gels say: Al - le - lu - ia!
Where, O death, is now thy sting? Al - le - lu - ia!
Fought the fight, the bat - tle won; Al - le - lu - ia!
Fol - l'wing our ex - alt - ed Head; Al - le - lu - ia!
Raise your joys and tri - umphs high, Al - le - lu - ia!
Dy - ing once, He all doth save: Al - le - lu - ia!
Death in vain for - bids Him rise; Al - le - lu - ia!
Made like Him, like Him we rise; Al - le - lu - ia!
Sing, ye heav'ns, and earth re - ply, Al - le - lu - ia!
Where thy vic - to - ry, O grave? Al - le - lu - ia!
Christ has o - pened Par - a - dise. Al - le - lu - ia!
Ours the cross, the grave, the skies. Al - le - lu - ia!

220 AMERICA THE BEAUTIFUL

KATHARINE LEE BATES
SAMUEL A. WARD
1. O beau - ti - ful for spa-cious skies, For am - ber waves of grain; . . .
2. O beau - ti - ful for pil - grim feet, Whose stern, im-pas-sioned stress . . .
3. O beau - ti - ful for he - roes proved In lib - er - at - ing strife, . . .
4. O beau - ti - ful for pa - triot dream That sees be - yond the years . . . .
For pur - ple moun-tain maj - es - ties A - bove the fruit - ed plain!
A thor-ough-fare for free - dom beat A - cross the wil - der - ness!
Who more than self their coun-try loved, And mer - cy more than life!
Thine al - a - bas - ter cit - ies gleam Un-dimmed by hu - man tears!
A - mer - i - ca! A - mer - i - ca! God shed His grace on thee,
A - mer - i - ca! A - mer - i - ca! God mend thine ev - 'ry flaw,
A - mer - i - ca! A - mer - i - ca! May God thy gold re - fine
A - mer - i - ca! A - mer - i - ca! God shed His grace on thee,
And crown thy good with broth - er - hood From sea to shin - ing sea!
Con - firm thy soul in self - con - trol, Thy lib - er - ty in law!
Till all suc-cess be no - ble - ness, And ev - 'ry gain di - vine!
And crown thy good with broth - er - hood From sea to shin - ing sea!

GOD OF OUR FATHERS

NATIONAL HYMN. 10, 10, 10, 10

DANIEL C. ROBERTS, 1876 GEORGE W. WARREN, 1892

Trumpets, before each verse.

1. God of our fa - thers, whose al-might - y
2. Thy love di - vine hath led us in the
3. From war's a - larms, from dead - ly pes - ti -
4. Re - fresh Thy peo - ple on their toil - some

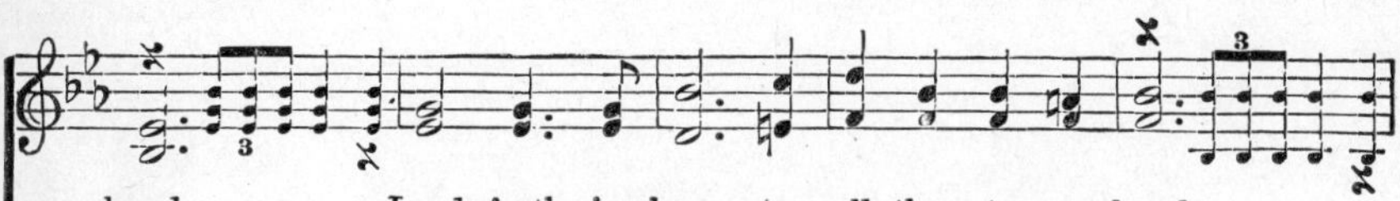

hand Leads forth in beau - ty all the star-ry band
past, In this free land by Thee our lot is cast;
lence, Be Thy strong arm our ev - er sure de - fense;
way, Lead us from night to nev - er - end - ing day;

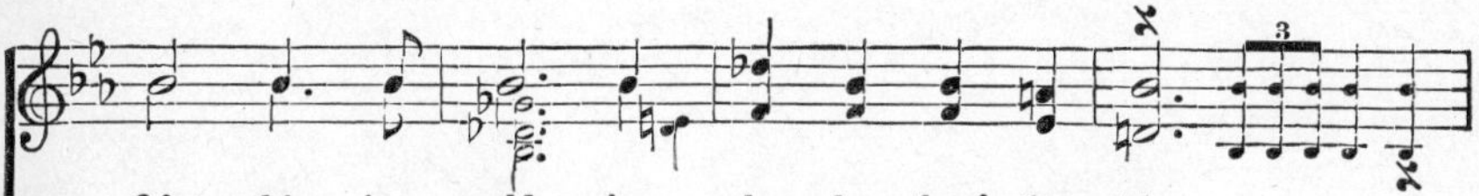

Of shin - ing worlds in splen - dor thro' the skies,
Be Thou our Rul - er, Guard - ian, Guide and Stay,
Thy true re - lig - ion in our hearts in - crease,
Fill all our lives with love and grace di - vine,

Our grate - ful songs be - fore Thy throne a - rise.
Thy word our law, Thy paths our cho - sen way.
Thy boun - teous good - ness nour - ish us in peace.
And glo - ry, laud and praise be ev - er Thine. A-men.

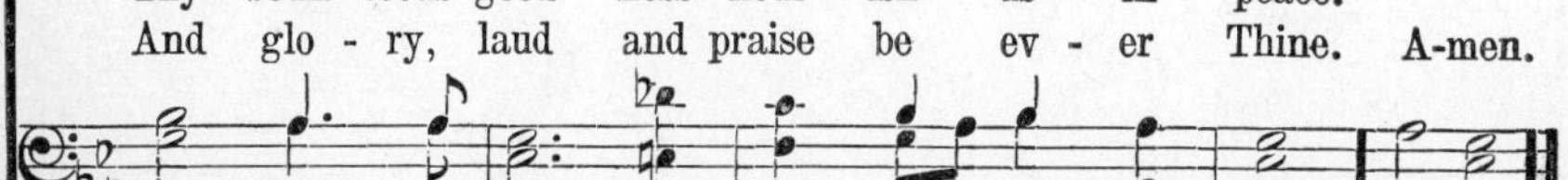

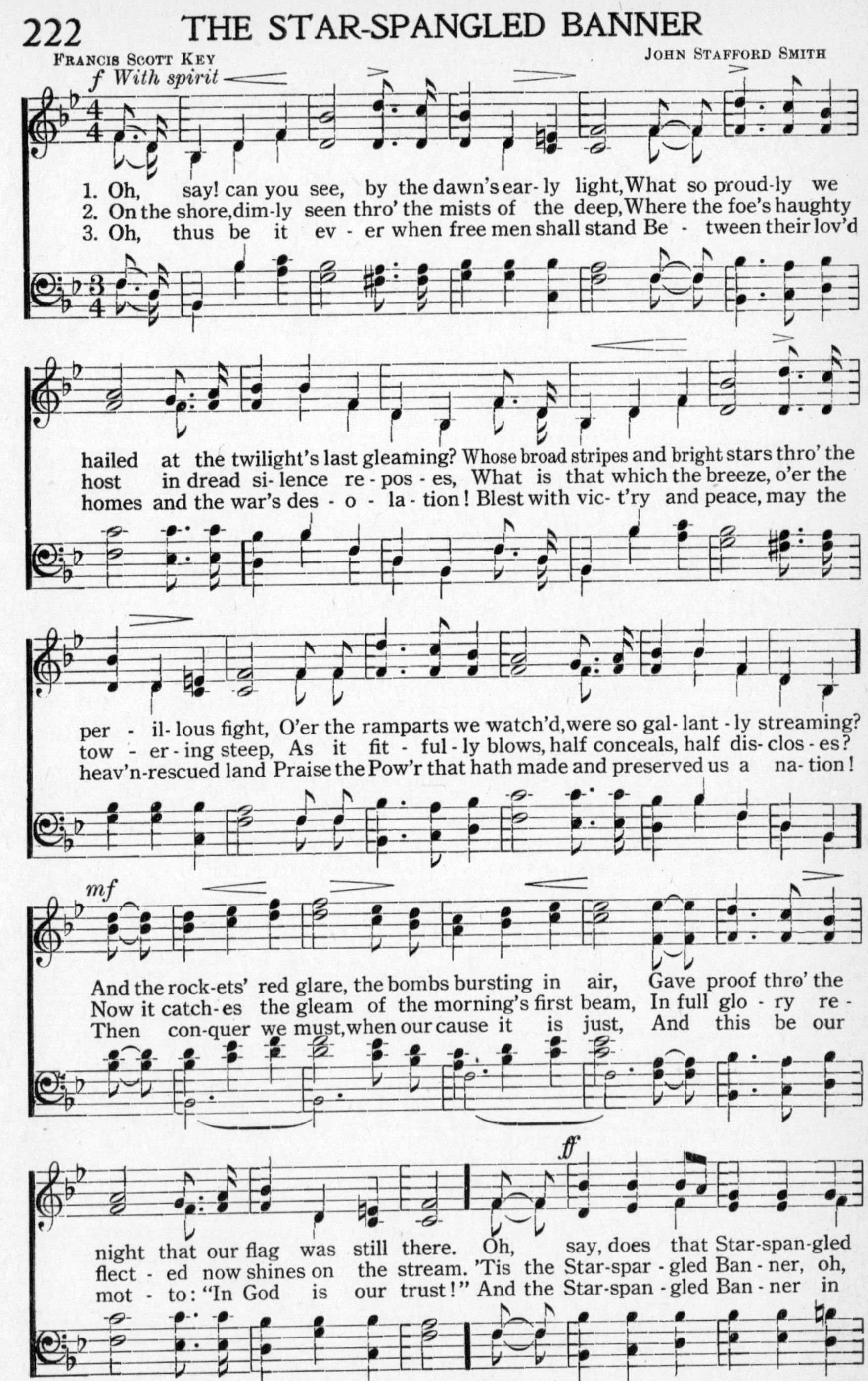
222 THE STAR-SPANGLED BANNER
FRANCIS SCOTT KEY
JOHN STAFFORD SMITH
f With spirit
1. Oh, say! can you see, by the dawn's ear-ly light, What so proud-ly we
2. On the shore, dim-ly seen thro' the mists of the deep, Where the foe's haughty
3. Oh, thus be it ev - er when free men shall stand Be - tween their lov'd
hailed at the twilight's last gleaming? Whose broad stripes and bright stars thro' the
host in dread si-lence re-pos-es, What is that which the breeze, o'er the
homes and the war's des - o - la-tion! Blest with vic-t'ry and peace, may the
per - il-lous fight, O'er the ramparts we watch'd, were so gal-lant-ly streaming?
tow - er-ing steep, As it fit - ful-ly blows, half conceals, half dis-clos-es?
heav'n-rescued land Praise the Pow'r that hath made and preserved us a na-tion!
mf
And the rock-ets' red glare, the bombs bursting in air, Gave proof thro' the
Now it catch-es the gleam of the morning's first beam, In full glo - ry re -
Then con-quer we must, when our cause it is just, And this be our
ff
night that our flag was still there. Oh, say, does that Star-span-gled
flect - ed now shines on the stream. 'Tis the Star-spar - gled Ban-ner, oh,
mot - to: "In God is our trust!" And the Star-span - gled Ban-ner in

THE STAR-SPANGLED BANNER

fff
Ban - ner still wave O'er the land of the free and the home of the brave?
long may it wave O'er the land of the free and the home of the brave!
tri - umph shall wave O'er the land of the free and the home of the brave!
223 MY COUNTRY, 'TIS OF THEE
Samuel F. Smith
Henry Carey
1. My coun - try, 'tis of thee, Sweet land of lib - er - ty,
2. My na - tive coun - try, thee, Land of the no - ble free,
3. Let mu - sic swell the breeze, And ring from all the trees
4. Our fa - thers' God! to Thee, Au - thor of lib - er - ty,
Of thee I sing; Land where my fa - thers died, Land of the
Thy name I love; I love thy rocks and rills, Thy woods and
Sweet freedom's song; Let mor - tal tongues a - wake; Let all that
To Thee we sing; Long may our land be bright With free-dom's
pil - grims' pride, From ev - 'ry moun - tain side Let free - dom ring!
tem - pled hills; My heart with rap - ture thrills Like that a - bove.
breathe par-take; Let rocks their si - lence break, The sound pro - long.
ho - ly light; Pro - tect us by Thy might, Great God, our King.

224 BATTLE HYMN OF THE REPUBLIC

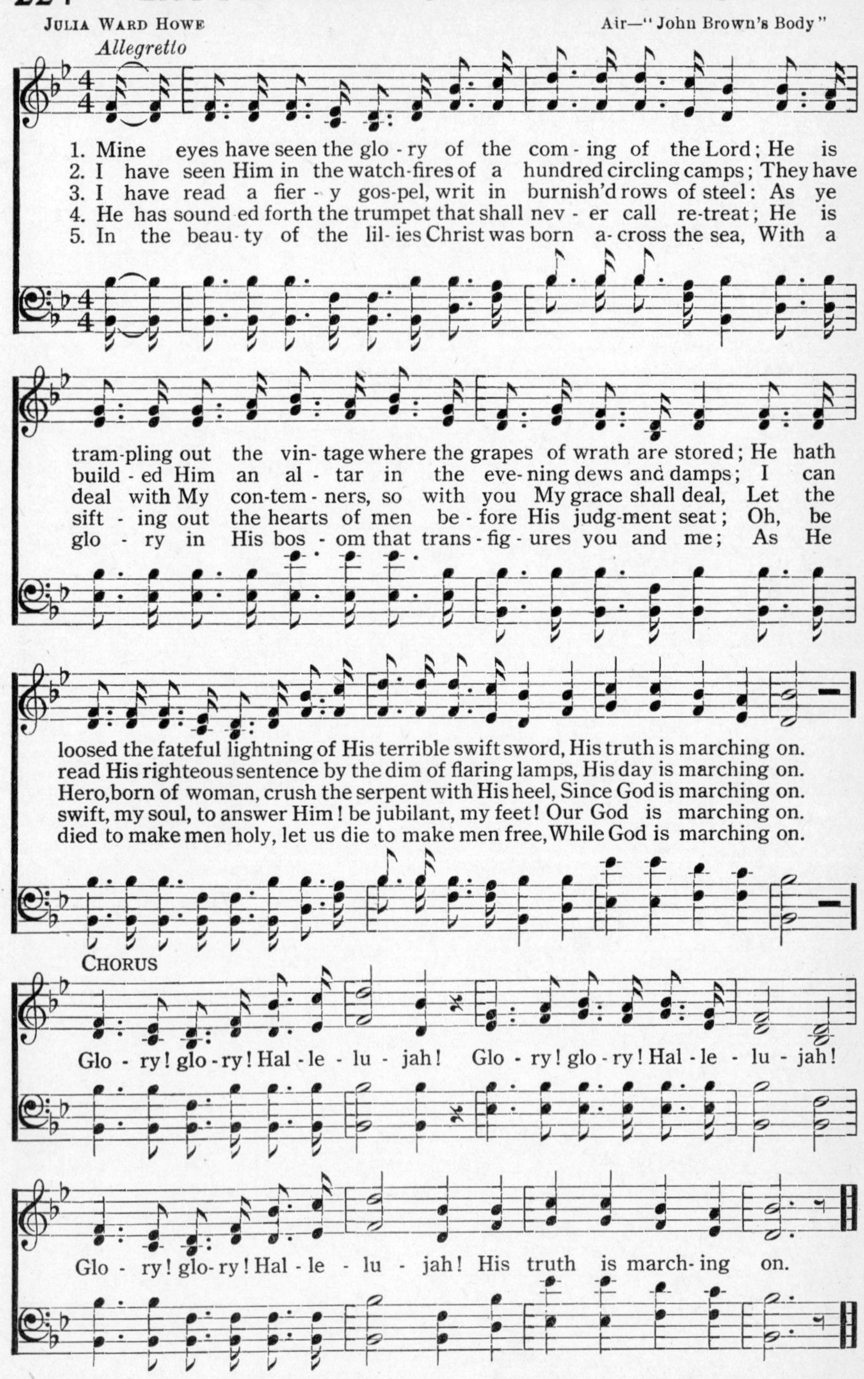
JULIA WARD HOWE
Air—"John Brown's Body"
Allegretto
1. Mine eyes have seen the glo - ry of the com - ing of the Lord; He is tram-pling out the vin- tage where the grapes of wrath are stored; He hath loosed the fateful lightning of His terrible swift sword, His truth is marching on.
2. I have seen Him in the watch-fires of a hundred circling camps; They have build - ed Him an al - tar in the eve- ning dews and damps; I can read His righteous sentence by the dim of flaring lamps, His day is marching on.
3. I have read a fier - y gos-pel, writ in burnish'd rows of steel: As ye deal with My con-tem - ners, so with you My grace shall deal, Let the Hero, born of woman, crush the serpent with His heel, Since God is marching on.
4. He has sound ed forth the trumpet that shall nev - er call re-treat; He is sift - ing out the hearts of men be - fore His judg-ment seat; Oh, be swift, my soul, to answer Him! be jubilant, my feet! Our God is marching on.
5. In the beau- ty of the lil- ies Christ was born a- cross the sea, With a glo - ry in His bos - om that trans - fig - ures you and me; As He died to make men holy, let us die to make men free, While God is marching on.
CHORUS
Glo - ry! glo - ry! Hal - le - lu - jah! Glo - ry! glo - ry! Hal - le - lu - jah!
Glo - ry! glo - ry! Hal - le - lu - jah! His truth is march- ing on.

SPIRITUALS

225 STANDIN' IN THE NEED OF PRAYER

DOWN BY THE RIVER-SIDE

5. Goin't' meet my dear old mother.
6. Goin't' meet my dear old father.
7. Goin't' meet dem Hebrew children.
8. Goin't' meet my loving Jesus.

227 LORD, I WANT TO BE A CHRISTIAN

228 WERE YOU THERE?

229 SWING LOW

Slow.

Swing low, sweet char - i - ot, Com - ing for to car - ry me
home; Swing low, sweet char - i - ot, Com-ing for to car-ry me home.
home; . . . .

FINE.

1. I looked o - ver Jor - dan, and what did I see,
2. If you get there be - fore I do,
3. I'm some - times up, I'm some - times down,

Com-ing for to car-ry me home? A band of an - gels
Com-ing for to car-ry me home; Tell all my friends I'm
Com-ing for to car-ry me home; But still my soul feels

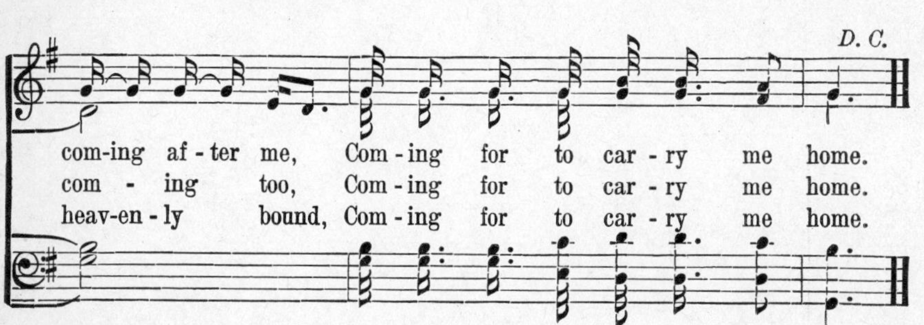

D. C.
com-ing af - ter me, Com - ing for to car - ry me home.
com - ing too, Com - ing for to car - ry me home.
heav-en - ly bound, Com - ing for to car - ry me home.

230 WALK IN JERUSALEM JUST LIKE JOHN

Arr. copyright, 1926, by Homer A. Rodeheaver   Arr. by J. B. HERBERT

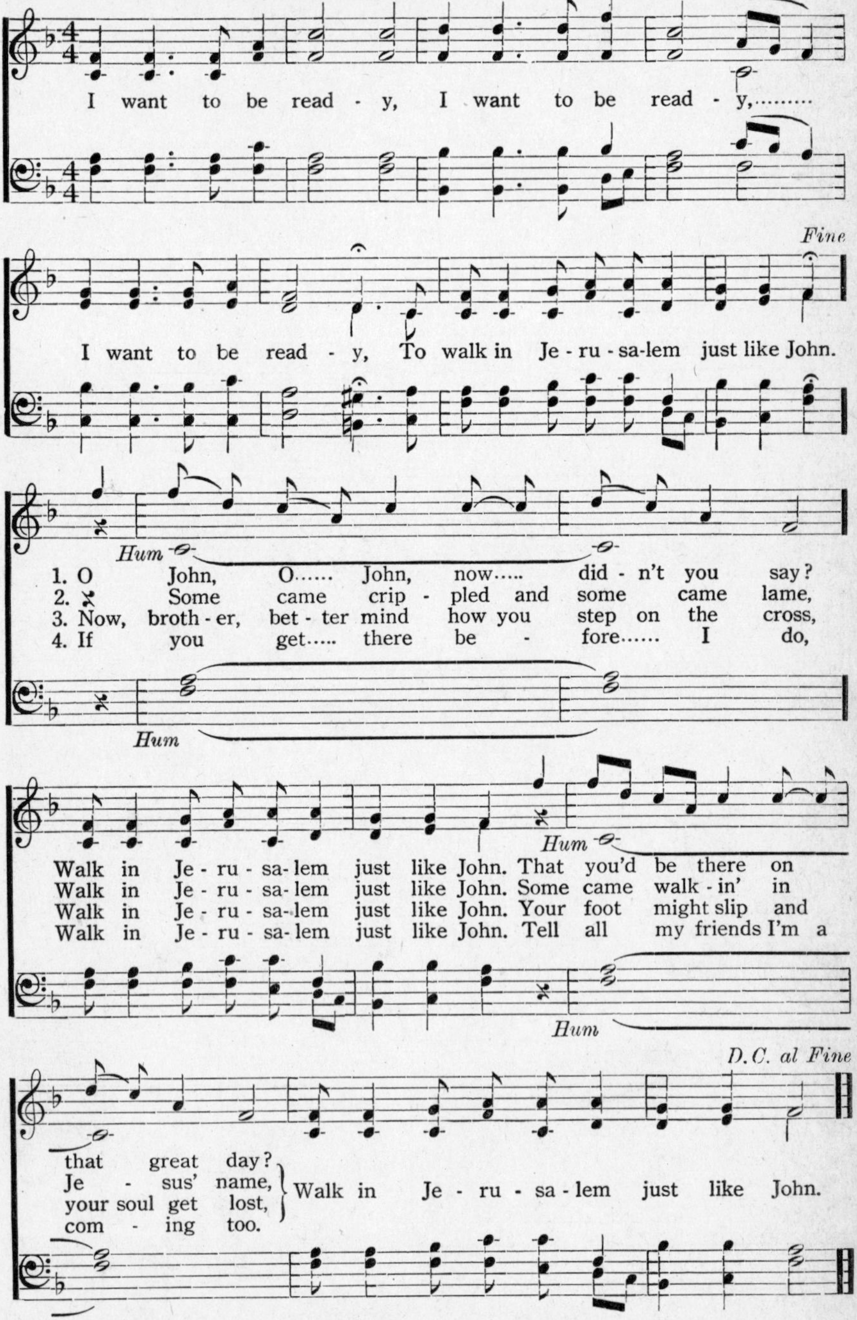
I want to be read - y, I want to be read - y,.........
I want to be read - y, To walk in Je - ru - sa-lem just like John.
Fine
Hum
1. O John, O...... John, now..... did - n't you say?
2. Some came crip - pled and some came lame,
3. Now, broth - er, bet - ter mind how you step on the cross,
4. If you get..... there be - fore...... I do,
Hum
Walk in Je - ru - sa-lem just like John. That you'd be there on
Walk in Je - ru - sa-lem just like John. Some came walk - in' in
Walk in Je - ru - sa-lem just like John. Your foot might slip and
Walk in Je - ru - sa-lem just like John. Tell all my friends I'm a
Hum
Hum
D.C. al Fine
that great day?
Je - sus' name,
your soul get lost,
com - ing too.
Walk in Je - ru - sa - lem just like John.

INDEX

INDEX

INDEX